ANATOMY OF FITNESS™

CYCLING
—LOGBOOK—
A Year-Long Training and Racing Journal

hinkler

Published by Hinkler Books Pty Ltd
45–55 Fairchild Street
Heatherton Victoria 3202 Australia
www.hinkler.com.au

hinkler

Image credits:
Images © Shutterstock.com: Cyclist riding a bicycle © Ljupco Smokovski; Mountain
bike on the hill © Farvatar; Woman during mountain biking trip © Florin Stana.

Cover design: Hinkler Design Studio
Illustrator: Hector Aiza/3DLabz
Prepress: Graphic Print Group

ISBN: 978 1 7436 3662 6

Printed and bound in China

It is recommended that you check with your doctor or healthcare professional
before commencing any exercise regime. While every care has been taken in
the preparation of this material, the publishers and their respective employees or
agents will not accept responsibility for injury or damage occasioned to any person
as a result of participation in the activities described in this book.

Introduction

Cycling is an incredibly rewarding activity. As a cyclist, you already know how wonderful a bike ride can make your body feel. During a good ride, your legs are pumping, your abdominal muscles are engaged, and a wide spectrum of different muscles is working hard. With its low impact on the joints and high rate of calorie burn, it is a great choice for anyone wanting to get (and stay) in shape. It is accessible to enthusiasts of all fitness levels: no matter what your capability when beginning or returning to the sport, cycling allows for all forms of progression, from riding a flat mile in the local park to completing a hilly 100-mile ride.

Cycling has also been known to boost mental health, decrease the risk of coronary heart disease, and improve coordination skills. Studies have connected cycling to the physical effects of decreased waistlines and prolonged caloric burn, and to heightened emotional health, mental capacity, and even earning potential and productivity at work.

Why use a logbook?

Keeping a record of your training is a great way to keep motivated, which helps you become a stronger, better cyclist. A logbook allows you to keep sight of the goals you set yourself when training. Looking back on what you've achieved over a few months or even week-to-week boosts your confidence and gives you the inspiration to keep working towards your goals. But don't become too focused on the numbers. Not only will that be a handicap to your training, you'll lose sight of the ultimate goal: having fun doing an activity you love.

A logbook makes it easy to flip through the pages to see what has or hasn't worked for you in the past and to compare your fitness levels across different time periods. Analyze your weekly and monthly results regularly and you'll see patterns emerging; use those patterns to identify your training behaviors and work to your strengths and weaknesses in a more targeted, effective way.

Using a logbook can help prevent overtraining and injury. By recording any soreness or aches you felt during your ride and reacting quickly to them, you could prevent more serious injuries. Going back through your logbook and discovering the cause of the injury helps you take preventative measures on future rides. This significantly reduces your risk of overtraining.

Your body has limits; it's crucial that you are aware of them. Ensure you alternate between easy days and hard days, and that there is a decent amount of difference between the training intensities of the two days. Trust your training and listen to your body; if it's telling you to slow down, then you should.

Setting goals

Start by asking what you want to achieve cycling-wise this year. Perhaps you want to work on your long-distance endurance or racing times or there's a competition you want to prepare for. Whatever is it, identify and write down 1–3 major points. Keep it short; having too long a list will likely complicate your training and demotivate you. These will be your goals for the coming year.

Your goals should be as specific as possible; avoid vague or broad statements like "I want to be better." Goals work best if they are measurable, performance-oriented and, most importantly, realistic. Challenge yourself, but within achievable limits. Set yourself a time frame: having a combination of short-term and long-term goals will keep you motivated and ensure you reach your targets. Remember, there's no better motivation than reaching your goals and seeing the results!

Dos and don'ts

- DON'T overtrain – it's important that listen to your body and don't wear it out too quickly. Allow enough recovery time between hard workouts.
- DO train consistently and moderately.
- DO get adequate rest – getting enough sleep is a necessity for a good workout.
- DON'T become dehydrated – ensure you have enough water throughout the day and during your ride.
- DON'T carry more food and water on your ride than you need.
- DO plan ahead – the checklist at the end of this logbook will help with that.
- DON'T lose sight of what cycling is all about – having fun!

Cycling and Nutrition

It's a common cycling adage to eat before you're hungry and drink before you're thirsty, and as a general rule this serves a good purpose. Because cycling is an endurance sport, it is critical to keep your body fueled. Begin your workout hydrated and stay that way throughout. Though experts disagree on the amount of fluids to be consumed during a workout, they agree that a lack of proper hydration will lead to a dramatic decrease in ability and performance.

People choose foods for a variety of reasons while they cycle. Some choices are made based on scientific principles of glycogen stores and uptake rates, while others are made based on the body's tolerance for certain ingredients when under stress. There are supplements and easily convertible carbohydrate gels, or there are simple peanut butter sandwiches. The choice is personal and best found through trial and error for your own goals.

During your ride

Generally, if you're going out for only an hour, don't stop for a calorie-rich peanut butter sandwich along the way. The body can store about 90 minutes worth of fuel to use.

However, while riding, you should be consuming carbohydrates. The body will extract glucose from carbohydrates much more easily than from protein or fat, so a high-fat choice of cream cheese on a bagel will only make you feel sluggish. The body works hard to get the glucose out of the fat, while it works easily getting it from dried fruit or a plain bagel.

A good rule of thumb is to consume carbohydrates every 30 minutes while on a prolonged ride, even if you're not feeling hungry. If you choose to use a sports gel, remember to drink plenty of water when you consume it. Cheaper than sports gels is the simple jelly bean. It's easy to digest, high in carbohydrates, and simple to eat while riding.

After your ride

The first 30 minutes after your ride are absolutely critical to replenishing glycogen stores. Some experts recommend taking your weight and dividing that figure in half to determine the number of carbohydrate grams you should consume in this window after riding. The window for replenishing these stores is literally only 30–60 minutes, so make sure to have recovery foods readily available. An excellent and scientifically sound choice for after your ride is low-fat chocolate milk. It's rich in carbohydrates and protein needed to help refuel and repair muscles, but should be consumed ideally within the first 30 minutes after finishing your workout.

A healthy diet

A well-planned, healthy diet that meets all nutritional needs is important for sporting and athletic performance. A good diet is made up of foods that are high in fiber and low in fat. A healthy diet focuses on a variety of foods that provide the body with the right amount of fuel and nutrition.

Everyone's nutritional needs vary, but below are some general daily guidelines.

Daily, women should aim to eat:

- 4–7 serves of vegetables
- 4–6 serves of wholegrain cereal, bread, rice, pasta, and noodles
- 2–3 serves of fruit
- 2–3 serves of low-fat milk, yogurt, cheese, and other dairy foods
- 1–1½ serves of eggs, legumes, and nuts
- 0–2½ serves of "extra" foods (high in fat, sugar, or salt)
- 3 pints (1.5L) of fluid.

Daily, men should aim to eat:

- 6–8 serves of vegetables
- 5–7 serves of wholegrain cereal, bread, rice, pasta, and noodles
- 3–4 serves of fruit
- 2–4 serves of low-fat milk, yogurt, cheese, and other dairy foods
- 1–1½ serves of eggs, legumes, and nuts
- 0–3 serves of "extra" foods (high in fat, sugar, or salt)
- 3 pints (1.5L) of fluid.

Try to eat lean meat and poultry only two or three times a week, and fish at least once or twice a week. Drink plenty of water and fluids to avoid dehydration. Drink coffee, tea and juice in moderation, as coffee and tea contain caffeine and juice contains kilojoules/calories.

To maintain a healthy diet, avoid:

- Fat, especially saturated fats
- Sugar and sugary food and drinks
- Fatty cuts of meat and processed meats
- Salt
- Alcohol (limit to one per day for women and two per day for men).

Stretches and Exercises

Regardless of your fitness level, the following stretches and exercises will help make you a better cyclist.

Stretches

Many athletes overlook the importance of stretching and flexibility. Getting the heart rate up or powering through a cycling routine often take center stage, but stretching plays a vital role in preventing stiffness and injury.

Latissmus dorsi stretch

1. Clasp your hands together above your head, your palms turned upwards towards the ceiling.
2. Reach your hands outwards as you make a circular pattern with your torso.
3. Slowly make a full circle. Repeat sequence three times in each direction.

Hip flexor stretch

1. Kneeling, bring one leg forwards, with your foot in front of your knee.
2. Slowly lean forwards and push your pelvis downwards until you feel a stretch in the front of your hip.
3. Hold for 15 seconds. Switch legs, and repeat, completing the sequence three times on each leg.

Spinal stretch

1. Lie on your back with your left leg straight and the right leg bent, placing your right foot on your left shin.

2. Keeping both shoulders on the floor, slowly bring your right leg across your body until you feel the stretch in the area between your lower back and hips. Stretch only as far as your shoulders will allow without one of them rising from the floor.

3. Hold for 15 seconds, and repeat sequence three times on each side.

Calf stretch

1. Stand with your feet parallel and close together, with your arms at your sides. Place a dumbbell on the floor in front of you.

2. Step forwards to place the toes of your left foot on the dumbbell bar. Lower your heel to the floor until you can feel a stretch.

3. Hold for 20 to 30 seconds, and repeat. Switch sides, and repeat on the right leg.

Iliotibal band stretch

1. Standing, cross your left leg in front of your right.

2. Bend at the waist while keeping both knees straight, and reach your hands towards the floor.

3. Hold for 15 seconds. Repeat sequence three times on each leg.

Quads stretch

1. Stand with your feet parallel and close together, with your arms at your sides.

2. With your right hand, reach behind as you bend your right knee. Grasp your right foot and gently pull your heel towards your buttocks with your hand until you feel a stretch in the front of your thigh. Keep both knees together and aligned.

3. Hold for 15 seconds, and repeat. Switch sides, and repeat on the left leg.

Intermediate Workout

You'll find this workout to be a valuable, plateau-defeating tool in your progression to cycling fitness.

Spinal twist

1. Sit on the floor, with your back straight. Extend your legs in front of you, slightly more than hip-width apart.
2. Lift yourself as tall as you can from the base of your spine. Ground your hips to the floor.
3. Lift up and out of your hips as you pull in your lower abdominals. Twist from your waist to the left, keeping your hips squared and grounded. Slowly return to the center.
4. Lift up and out of your hips again, twisting in the other direction.
5. Return to the center. Repeat three times in each direction.

Chair dip

1. Sit up tall near the front of a sturdy chair. Place your hands beside your hips, wrapping your fingers over the front edge of the chair.
2. Extend your legs in front of you slightly, and place your feet flat on the floor.
3. Scoot off the edge of the chair until your knees align directly above your feet and your torso will be able to clear the chair as you dip down.
4. Bending your elbows directly behind you (without splaying them out to the sides), lower your torso until your elbows make a 90-degree angle.
5. Raise your body back to the starting position. Repeat fifteen times.

Power squat

1. Stand upright, holding a weighted ball with both hands in front of your torso.
2. Shift your weight to your left foot, lifting your right foot toward your buttocks. Bend your elbows and draw the ball toward your right ear.
3. Maintaining a neutral spine, in which the three main curves of your back are all properly aligned, bend at your hips and knee. Lower your torso toward your left side, bringing the ball toward your right ankle.

4. Press into your left leg and straighten your knee and torso, returning to the starting position. Repeat fifteen times on each leg.

Wall sit

1. Stand with your back against a wall. Walk your feet out from under your body until your lower back rests comfortably against the wall.

2. Slide your torso down the wall, until your hips and knees form 90-degree angles, and your thighs are parallel to the floor.

3. Raise your arms straight in front of you so that they are parallel to your thighs, and relax the upper torso. Hold for one minute, and repeat five times.

Scissors

1. Lie with your back on the floor, your arms by your sides and your legs raised with the knees bent so that your thighs are perpendicular to the floor and your shins are parallel to the floor. Inhale, drawing in your abdominals.

2. Reach your legs straight up, and lift your head and shoulders off the floor.

3. Extending your right leg away from your body, raise your left leg towards your trunk. Hold your left calf with your hands and bring it towards you in a pulsing action twice while keeping your shoulders down.

4. Switch your legs in the air, reaching for your right leg. Stabilize your pelvis and spine. Repeat sequence six to eight times on each leg.

Single-leg kick

1. Lie prone on the mat with your arms flexed and elbows directly under your shoulders. Lengthen your legs and keep them adducted together.

2. Inhale, drawing your navel in towards your spine. Exhale, bending one knee. Point your foot and pulse your bent leg eight times.

3. Exhale, then flex your foot and pulse an additional eight times.

4. Inhale, straightening your bent leg on the mat next to your other leg. Exhale, bending your opposite leg, and repeat. Repeat the entire sequence six to eight times.

Push-up

1. Stand straight, inhale, and pull your navel to your spine. Exhale as you roll down one vertebra at a time until your hands touch the floor in front of you.

2. Walk your hands out until they are directly beneath your shoulders in the plank position.

3. Inhale, and "set" your body by drawing your abdominals toward your spine. Squeeze your buttocks and legs together and stretch out of your heels, bringing your body into a straight line.

4. Exhale as you bend your elbows and lower your body toward the floor. Then inhale as you push upwards to return to plank position. Keep your elbows close to your body. Repeat eight times.

5. Inhale as you lift your hips into the air, and walk your hands back toward your feet. Exhale slowly, rolling up one vertebra at a time into your starting position. Repeat the entire exercise three times.

Hamstrings stretch

1. Lie on your back with both knees bent and your feet flat on the floor.

2. Grasp your left leg behind the knee, and draw your knee in towards your chest.

3. Keeping your knee pulled into your chest, flex your toes, contract your quadriceps, and begin to straighten your leg.

4. Release your leg into the stretch, and pull it closer towards your chest. Repeat ten times on each leg.

Plank press-up

1. Lying on the mat with your forearms underneath your chest, press your body up into a plank position, lengthening through your heels.

2. Push through your forearms to bring your shoulders up towards the ceiling. With control, lower your shoulders until you feel them coming together in your back. Repeat five times.

Plank knee pull-in

1. Start in the plank position, with your shoulders directly over your hands, your torso straight.
2. Draw your left knee into your chest, flexing the foot while rocking your body forwards over your hands. You should come up on the toes of your right foot.
3. Extend your left knee backwards, rocking the body back, and shifting your weight onto your right heel. With your head in between your hands, straighten your right leg and lift it towards the ceiling. Repeat ten times on each leg.

How to Use this Logbook

This logbook is designed to be complete record of your cycling sessions and results over twelve months. It is divided into days, weeks, months, and a year so you can monitor cycling practices and behaviors. As the logbook is not dated, start recording information at any time.

Annual hours planner

The logbook starts with a twelve-month planner to record your projected hours over the course of a year. You can also use it to record projected miles, if you prefer working with distance rather than time. Fill in major events and occurrences that could affect your cycling sessions throughout the year.

Yearly assessments

Record your details at the start and end of the twelve-month period covered by the logbook. Use the first assessment page at the beginning of your program to set out your measurements and targets. The end-of-year assessment lets you assess whether you've met or surpassed those goals.

Weekly records

The weekly record forms the major part of the logbook. Set weekly targets and record basic information like time, distance, speed, route, and weight. There's also space to record more subjective information and vital signs like energy level, mood, soreness, and a ride report. At the end of each week, add up the totals to show your overall results and compare it against your goal from the start of the week.

Monthly evaluation

Use the monthly evaluation pages to set goals and measure your progress over the past month. By assessing your fitness and goals at the start of the month and comparing it against your results at the end of the month, you'll not only have a great idea of your progress but also be motivated to keep up the good work!

Yearly heart-rate graph

The heart-rate graph is a great visual way to track your fitness over the course of twelve months. Each week, simply mark your resting and maximum heart rates on the graph. As the year progresses, you'll get a good idea of how you are doing with your cycling program.

Personal bests

At the end of the year, record your best times and results in this section. Use this information to help set new goals and targets for the next twelve months.

Training and pre-ride checklist

Before each ride, use the training checklist on page 256 to ensure you have everything you need for a fun and safe ride. Use the pre-ride inspection checklist to ensure your bike is in good working order.

Terms used in this logbook

Resting heart rate

Record your resting heart rate. The best time to measure your resting heart rate is 2–3 minutes after you wake up in the morning. You can measure this with a heart rate monitor. If you don't have one, check your resting heart rate by finding your pulse with your index and middle fingers and counting how many beats occur in ten seconds, then multiply that number by six. For example, you count eight beats in ten seconds: 8 x 6 = a resting heart rate of 48bpm.

Zone

Use this section to record your heart rate training zone. The zones are calculated based on your maximum heart rate (MHR). The most accurate way of determining your MHR is to have it clinically tested by a doctor or exercise professional, but you can find a rough estimate by calculating it as 220 heart beats per minute minus your age.

Zone 1	less than 55% of MHR
Zone 2	56–75% of MHR
Zone 3	76–90% of MHR
Zone 4	91–100% of MHR
Zone 5a	101–105% of MHR
Zone 5b	106–120% of MHR
Zone 5c	more than 121% of MHR

Rated perceived effort (RPE)

Rate your perceived effort on a scale of 1 to 10, with 10 being maximum effort exerted.

Time, distance, inclination and speed

Record the number of hours, minutes and seconds covered in the ride, as well as the number of miles covered. Be as exact as possible. Also record the incline and the average and maximum speeds; you can calculate these using a cycling computer or bike calculator.

Weight

Record your current weight. You may prefer to only record this information once a week, once a fortnight, or once a month.

Food and water intake

Record what you eat and drink during your ride, and also if nothing was consumed.

Energy, stress and mood

Rate your energy and stress levels from 1 to 5, with 5 being the most energetic and most stressed ratings. Describe your mood during your ride. Remember, a bad mood can affect performance!

Sleep hours and quality

Record how many hours you slept the night before a ride. Rate the quality of your sleep on a scale of 1 to 5, with 5 being the best rating. Note that many phones have an app to determine your sleep quality and patterns for more accurate results.

Soreness, injuries and illnesses

Rate your soreness after your ride on a scale of 1 to 5, with 5 being the sorest rating. List any injuries or illnesses that may affect your cycling, like having the flu, an ache in your wrist, etc.

Route and weather

Write a brief description of the route (street names, track or park name, general area, etc.). Describe the weather during your ride; you may also like to record the exact temperature.

Ride report

Write a short description of your ride. This section should include information not previously covered in the daily record. Be sure to include anything you feel is important.

The Muscular System

The human body contains more than 600 muscles. Each muscle performs a particular function, and they all work together to operate the human body.

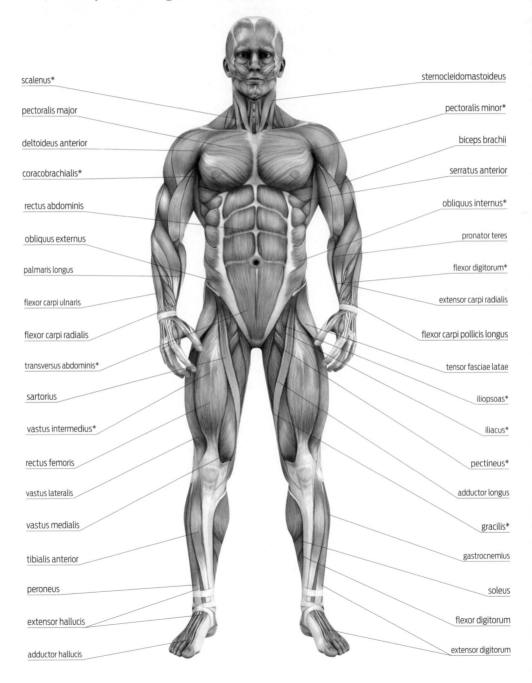

scalenus*

pectoralis major

deltoideus anterior

coracobrachialis*

rectus abdominis

obliquus externus

palmaris longus

flexor carpi ulnaris

flexor carpi radialis

transversus abdominis*

sartorius

vastus intermedius*

rectus femoris

vastus lateralis

vastus medialis

tibialis anterior

peroneus

extensor hallucis

adductor hallucis

sternocleidomastoideus

pectoralis minor*

biceps brachii

serratus anterior

obliquus internus*

pronator teres

flexor digitorum*

extensor carpi radialis

flexor carpi pollicis longus

tensor fasciae latae

iliopsoas*

iliacus*

pectineus*

adductor longus

gracilis*

gastrocnemius

soleus

flexor digitorum

extensor digitorum

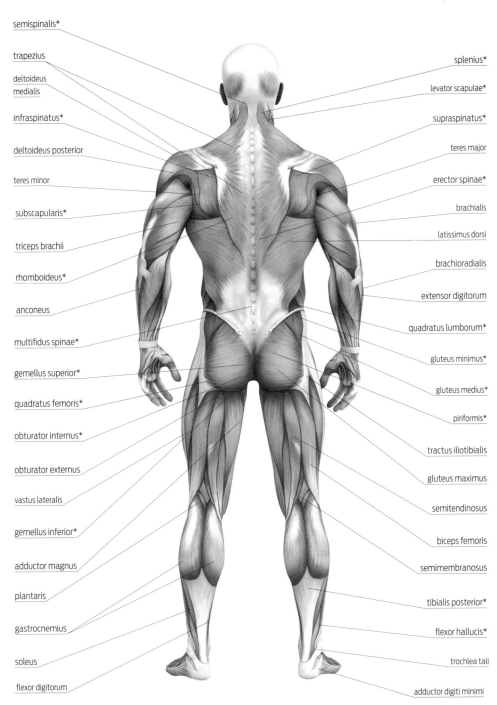

semispinalis*

trapezius

deltoideus
medialis

infraspinatus*

deltoideus posterior

teres minor

subscapularis*

triceps brachii

rhomboideus*

anconeus

multifidus spinae*

gemellus superior*

quadratus femoris*

obturator internus*

obturator externus

vastus lateralis

gemellus inferior*

adductor magnus

plantaris

gastrocnemius

soleus

flexor digitorum

splenius*

levator scapulae*

supraspinatus*

teres major

erector spinae*

brachialis

latissimus dorsi

brachioradialis

extensor digitorum

quadratus lumborum*

gluteus minimus*

gluteus medius*

piriformis*

tractus iliotibialis

gluteus maximus

semitendinosus

biceps femoris

semimembranosus

tibialis posterior*

flexor hallucis*

trochlea tali

adductor digiti minimi

Annual Hours Planner

	JANUARY	FEBRUARY	MARCH	APRIL	MAY	JUNE
1						
2						
3						
4						
5						
6						
7						
8						
9						
10						
11						
12						
13						
14						
15						
16						
17						
18						
19						
20						
21						
22						
23						
24						
25						
26						
27						
28						
29						
30						
31						
	JANUARY	FEBRUARY	MARCH	APRIL	MAY	JUNE

JULY	AUGUST	SEPTEMBER	OCTOBER	NOVEMBER	DECEMBER	
						1
						2
						3
						4
						5
						6
						7
						8
						9
						10
						11
						12
						13
						14
						15
						16
						17
						18
						19
						20
						21
						22
						23
						24
						25
						26
						27
						28
						29
						30
						31
JULY	AUGUST	SEPTEMBER	OCTOBER	NOVEMBER	DECEMBER	

Start-of-Year Assessment

DATE / /   **AGE**

Record your results from your first ride in the logbook here: this will be your starting point against which your subsequent results are measured.

Current Stats	
Weight	
Resting heart rate	
Total distance	
Total time	
Average zone	
Average speed	
Maximum speed	
Inclination	
RPE	

Target Stats	
Weight	
Resting heart rate	
Total distance	
Total time	
Average zone	
Average speed	
Maximum speed	
Inclination	
RPE	

Cardiovascular Fitness Test

Use the same course each time.

- Record your resting heart rate before warming up
- Complete the course as fast as you can, recording your working heart rate every 4 minutes
- Still standing, record your recovery heart rate when you finish and then 1, 2, and 3 minutes after you finish
- Record the time it took to finish the course.

Cardiovascular Fitness Test		
	Current	Target
Resting heart rate		
Working heart rate: after 4 minutes		
after 8 minutes		
after 12 minutes		
Recovery heart rate: at course completion		
1 minute after completion		
2 minutes after completion		
3 minutes after completion		
Time to cycle 3 miles/5km		
Completion time		

Current Personal Summary

Strength level — 1–5 [ ]

Endurance level — 1–5 [ ]

Satisfaction with fitness — 1–5 [ ]

Satisfaction with weight — 1–5 [ ]

Quality of diet — 1–5 [ ]

Energy level — 1–5 [ ]

Sleep quality — 1–5 [ ]

Stress level — 1–5 [ ]

Mood level — 1–5 [ ]

Personal Goals

Week Beginning

/ /

MONDAY			
Energy	Sleep (hrs)	Sleep quality	Stress
Mood	Weather	Soreness	Weight
Injury/illness			

Ride 1	Ride 2
Resting heart rate:	Resting heart rate:
Route:	Route:
Distance:	Distance:
Time:	Time:
Zone: 1 2 3 4 5	Zone: 1 2 3 4 5
Average speed:	Average speed:
Max speed:	Max speed:
Inclination:	Inclination:
Food and water intake:	Food and water intake:
Ride report:	Ride report:
RPE: 1 – 10	RPE: 1 – 10

TUESDAY			
Energy	Sleep (hrs)	Sleep quality	Stress
Mood	Weather	Soreness	Weight
Injury/illness			

Ride 1	Ride 2
Resting heart rate:	Resting heart rate:
Route:	Route:
Distance:	Distance:
Time:	Time:
Zone: 1 2 3 4 5	Zone: 1 2 3 4 5
Average speed:	Average speed:
Max speed:	Max speed:
Inclination:	Inclination:
Food and water intake:	Food and water intake:
Ride report:	Ride report:
RPE: 1 – 10	RPE: 1 – 10

Weekly Goals

WEDNESDAY			
Energy	Sleep (hrs)	Sleep quality	Stress
Mood	Weather	Soreness	Weight
Injury/illness			

Ride 1	Ride 2
Resting heart rate:	Resting heart rate:
Route:	Route:
Distance:	Distance:
Time:	Time:
Zone: 1 2 3 4 5	Zone: 1 2 3 4 5
Average speed:	Average speed:
Max speed:	Max speed:
Inclination:	Inclination:
Food and water intake:	Food and water intake:
Ride report:	Ride report:
RPE: 1 – 10	RPE: 1 – 10

THURSDAY			
Energy	Sleep (hrs)	Sleep quality	Stress
Mood	Weather	Soreness	Weight
Injury/illness			

Ride 1	Ride 2
Resting heart rate:	Resting heart rate:
Route:	Route:
Distance:	Distance:
Time:	Time:
Zone: 1 2 3 4 5	Zone: 1 2 3 4 5
Average speed:	Average speed:
Max speed:	Max speed:
Inclination:	Inclination:
Food and water intake:	Food and water intake:
Ride report:	Ride report:
RPE: 1 – 10	RPE: 1 – 10

Week Beginning / / Continued

FRIDAY			
Energy	Sleep (hrs)	Sleep quality	Stress
Mood	Weather	Soreness	Weight
Injury/illness			

Ride 1	Ride 2
Resting heart rate:	Resting heart rate:
Route:	Route:
Distance:	Distance:
Time:	Time:
Zone: 1 2 3 4 5	Zone: 1 2 3 4 5
Average speed:	Average speed:
Max speed:	Max speed:
Inclination:	Inclination:
Food and water intake:	Food and water intake:
Ride report:	Ride report:
RPE: 1 – 10	RPE: 1 – 10

SATURDAY			
Energy	Sleep (hrs)	Sleep quality	Stress
Mood	Weather	Soreness	Weight
Injury/illness			

Ride 1	Ride 2
Resting heart rate:	Resting heart rate:
Route:	Route:
Distance:	Distance:
Time:	Time:
Zone: 1 2 3 4 5	Zone: 1 2 3 4 5
Average speed:	Average speed:
Max speed:	Max speed:
Inclination:	Inclination:
Food and water intake:	Food and water intake:
Ride report:	Ride report:
RPE: 1 – 10	RPE: 1 – 10

SUNDAY			
Energy	Sleep (hrs)	Sleep quality	Stress
Mood	Weather	Soreness	Weight
Injury/illness			

Ride 1	Ride 2
Resting heart rate:	Resting heart rate:
Route:	Route:
Distance:	Distance:
Time:	Time:
Zone: 1 2 3 4 5	Zone: 1 2 3 4 5
Average speed:	Average speed:
Max speed:	Max speed:
Inclination:	Inclination:
Food and water intake:	Food and water intake:
Ride report:	Ride report:
RPE: 1 – 10	RPE: 1 – 10

WEEKLY COMPETITION	
Race 1	Race 2
Time Goal:	Time Goal:
Resting heart rate:	Resting heart rate:
Weather:	Weather:
Route:	Route:
Distance:	Distance:
Time:	Time:
Zone: 1 2 3 4 5	Zone: 1 2 3 4 5
Average speed:	Average speed:
Inclination:	Inclination:
Notes:	Notes:

WEEKLY SUMMARY		
Weight	Distance	Time
Average speed	RPE: 1 – 10	
Notes:		

Week Beginning

MONDAY			
Energy	Sleep (hrs)	Sleep quality	Stress
Mood	Weather	Soreness	Weight
Injury/illness			

Ride 1	Ride 2
Resting heart rate:	Resting heart rate:
Route:	Route:
Distance:	Distance:
Time:	Time:
Zone: 1 2 3 4 5	Zone: 1 2 3 4 5
Average speed:	Average speed:
Max speed:	Max speed:
Inclination:	Inclination:
Food and water intake:	Food and water intake:
Ride report:	Ride report:
RPE: 1 – 10	RPE: 1 – 10

TUESDAY			
Energy	Sleep (hrs)	Sleep quality	Stress
Mood	Weather	Soreness	Weight
Injury/illness			

Ride 1	Ride 2
Resting heart rate:	Resting heart rate:
Route:	Route:
Distance:	Distance:
Time:	Time:
Zone: 1 2 3 4 5	Zone: 1 2 3 4 5
Average speed:	Average speed:
Max speed:	Max speed:
Inclination:	Inclination:
Food and water intake:	Food and water intake:
Ride report:	Ride report:
RPE: 1 – 10	RPE: 1 – 10

Weekly Goals

WEDNESDAY			
Energy	Sleep (hrs)	Sleep quality	Stress
Mood	Weather	Soreness	Weight
Injury/illness			

Ride 1	Ride 2
Resting heart rate:	Resting heart rate:
Route:	Route:
Distance:	Distance:
Time:	Time:
Zone: 1 2 3 4 5	Zone: 1 2 3 4 5
Average speed:	Average speed:
Max speed:	Max speed:
Inclination:	Inclination:
Food and water intake:	Food and water intake:
Ride report:	Ride report:
RPE: 1 – 10	RPE: 1 – 10

THURSDAY			
Energy	Sleep (hrs)	Sleep quality	Stress
Mood	Weather	Soreness	Weight
Injury/illness			

Ride 1	Ride 2
Resting heart rate:	Resting heart rate:
Route:	Route:
Distance:	Distance:
Time:	Time:
Zone: 1 2 3 4 5	Zone: 1 2 3 4 5
Average speed:	Average speed:
Max speed:	Max speed:
Inclination:	Inclination:
Food and water intake:	Food and water intake:
Ride report:	Ride report:
RPE: 1 – 10	RPE: 1 – 10

Week Beginning Continued

FRIDAY			
Energy	Sleep (hrs)	Sleep quality	Stress
Mood	Weather	Soreness	Weight
Injury/illness			

Ride 1	Ride 2
Resting heart rate:	Resting heart rate:
Route:	Route:
Distance:	Distance:
Time:	Time:
Zone: 1 2 3 4 5	Zone: 1 2 3 4 5
Average speed:	Average speed:
Max speed:	Max speed:
Inclination:	Inclination:
Food and water intake:	Food and water intake:
Ride report:	Ride report:
RPE: 1 – 10	RPE: 1 – 10

SATURDAY			
Energy	Sleep (hrs)	Sleep quality	Stress
Mood	Weather	Soreness	Weight
Injury/illness			

Ride 1	Ride 2
Resting heart rate:	Resting heart rate:
Route:	Route:
Distance:	Distance:
Time:	Time:
Zone: 1 2 3 4 5	Zone: 1 2 3 4 5
Average speed:	Average speed:
Max speed:	Max speed:
Inclination:	Inclination:
Food and water intake:	Food and water intake:
Ride report:	Ride report:
RPE: 1 – 10	RPE: 1 – 10

SUNDAY			
Energy	Sleep (hrs)	Sleep quality	Stress
Mood	Weather	Soreness	Weight
Injury/illness			

Ride 1	Ride 2
Resting heart rate:	Resting heart rate:
Route:	Route:
Distance:	Distance:
Time:	Time:
Zone: 1 2 3 4 5	Zone: 1 2 3 4 5
Average speed:	Average speed:
Max speed:	Max speed:
Inclination:	Inclination:
Food and water intake:	Food and water intake:
Ride report:	Ride report:
RPE: 1 – 10	RPE: 1 – 10

WEEKLY COMPETITION	
Race 1	Race 2
Time Goal:	Time Goal:
Resting heart rate:	Resting heart rate:
Weather:	Weather:
Route:	Route:
Distance:	Distance:
Time:	Time:
Zone: 1 2 3 4 5	Zone: 1 2 3 4 5
Average speed:	Average speed:
Inclination:	Inclination:
Notes:	Notes:

WEEKLY SUMMARY		
Weight	Distance	Time
Average speed	RPE: 1 – 10	
Notes:		

Week Beginning

 / /

MONDAY			
Energy	Sleep (hrs)	Sleep quality	Stress
Mood	Weather	Soreness	Weight
Injury/illness			

Ride 1	Ride 2
Resting heart rate:	Resting heart rate:
Route:	Route:
Distance:	Distance:
Time:	Time:
Zone: 1 2 3 4 5	Zone: 1 2 3 4 5
Average speed:	Average speed:
Max speed:	Max speed:
Inclination:	Inclination:
Food and water intake:	Food and water intake:
Ride report:	Ride report:
RPE: 1 – 10	RPE: 1 – 10

TUESDAY			
Energy	Sleep (hrs)	Sleep quality	Stress
Mood	Weather	Soreness	Weight
Injury/illness			

Ride 1	Ride 2
Resting heart rate:	Resting heart rate:
Route:	Route:
Distance:	Distance:
Time:	Time:
Zone: 1 2 3 4 5	Zone: 1 2 3 4 5
Average speed:	Average speed:
Max speed:	Max speed:
Inclination:	Inclination:
Food and water intake:	Food and water intake:
Ride report:	Ride report:
RPE: 1 – 10	RPE: 1 – 10

Weekly Goals

WEDNESDAY			
Energy	Sleep (hrs)	Sleep quality	Stress
Mood	Weather	Soreness	Weight
Injury/illness			

Ride 1	Ride 2
Resting heart rate:	Resting heart rate:
Route:	Route:
Distance:	Distance:
Time:	Time:
Zone: 1 2 3 4 5	Zone: 1 2 3 4 5
Average speed:	Average speed:
Max speed:	Max speed:
Inclination:	Inclination:
Food and water intake:	Food and water intake:
Ride report:	Ride report:
RPE: 1 – 10	RPE: 1 – 10

THURSDAY			
Energy	Sleep (hrs)	Sleep quality	Stress
Mood	Weather	Soreness	Weight
Injury/illness			

Ride 1	Ride 2
Resting heart rate:	Resting heart rate:
Route:	Route:
Distance:	Distance:
Time:	Time:
Zone: 1 2 3 4 5	Zone: 1 2 3 4 5
Average speed:	Average speed:
Max speed:	Max speed:
Inclination:	Inclination:
Food and water intake:	Food and water intake:
Ride report:	Ride report:
RPE: 1 – 10	RPE: 1 – 10

Week Beginning  / / Continued

FRIDAY			
Energy	Sleep (hrs)	Sleep quality	Stress
Mood	Weather	Soreness	Weight
Injury/illness			

Ride 1	Ride 2
Resting heart rate:	Resting heart rate:
Route:	Route:
Distance:	Distance:
Time:	Time:
Zone: 1 2 3 4 5	Zone: 1 2 3 4 5
Average speed:	Average speed:
Max speed:	Max speed:
Inclination:	Inclination:
Food and water intake:	Food and water intake:
Ride report:	Ride report:
RPE: 1 – 10	RPE: 1 – 10

SATURDAY			
Energy	Sleep (hrs)	Sleep quality	Stress
Mood	Weather	Soreness	Weight
Injury/illness			

Ride 1	Ride 2
Resting heart rate:	Resting heart rate:
Route:	Route:
Distance:	Distance:
Time:	Time:
Zone: 1 2 3 4 5	Zone: 1 2 3 4 5
Average speed:	Average speed:
Max speed:	Max speed:
Inclination:	Inclination:
Food and water intake:	Food and water intake:
Ride report:	Ride report:
RPE: 1 – 10	RPE: 1 – 10

SUNDAY

Energy		Sleep (hrs)		Sleep quality		Stress	
Mood		Weather		Soreness		Weight	
Injury/illness							

Ride 1	Ride 2
Resting heart rate:	Resting heart rate:
Route:	Route:
Distance:	Distance:
Time:	Time:
Zone: 1 2 3 4 5	Zone: 1 2 3 4 5
Average speed:	Average speed:
Max speed:	Max speed:
Inclination:	Inclination:
Food and water intake:	Food and water intake:
Ride report:	Ride report:
RPE: 1 – 10	RPE: 1 – 10

WEEKLY COMPETITION

Race 1	Race 2
Time Goal:	Time Goal:
Resting heart rate:	Resting heart rate:
Weather:	Weather:
Route:	Route:
Distance:	Distance:
Time:	Time:
Zone: 1 2 3 4 5	Zone: 1 2 3 4 5
Average speed:	Average speed:
Inclination:	Inclination:
Notes:	Notes:

WEEKLY SUMMARY

Weight		Distance		Time	
Average speed		RPE: 1 – 10			
Notes:					

Week Beginning

 / /

MONDAY			
Energy	Sleep (hrs)	Sleep quality	Stress
Mood	Weather	Soreness	Weight
Injury/illness			

Ride 1	Ride 2
Resting heart rate:	Resting heart rate:
Route:	Route:
Distance:	Distance:
Time:	Time:
Zone: 1 2 3 4 5	Zone: 1 2 3 4 5
Average speed:	Average speed:
Max speed:	Max speed:
Inclination:	Inclination:
Food and water intake:	Food and water intake:
Ride report:	Ride report:
RPE: 1 – 10	RPE: 1 – 10

TUESDAY			
Energy	Sleep (hrs)	Sleep quality	Stress
Mood	Weather	Soreness	Weight
Injury/illness			

Ride 1	Ride 2
Resting heart rate:	Resting heart rate:
Route:	Route:
Distance:	Distance:
Time:	Time:
Zone: 1 2 3 4 5	Zone: 1 2 3 4 5
Average speed:	Average speed:
Max speed:	Max speed:
Inclination:	Inclination:
Food and water intake:	Food and water intake:
Ride report:	Ride report:
RPE: 1 – 10	RPE: 1 – 10

Weekly Goals

WEDNESDAY			
Energy	Sleep (hrs)	Sleep quality	Stress
Mood	Weather	Soreness	Weight
Injury/illness			

Ride 1	Ride 2
Resting heart rate:	Resting heart rate:
Route:	Route:
Distance:	Distance:
Time:	Time:
Zone: 1 2 3 4 5	Zone: 1 2 3 4 5
Average speed:	Average speed:
Max speed:	Max speed:
Inclination:	Inclination:
Food and water intake:	Food and water intake:
Ride report:	Ride report:
RPE: 1 – 10	RPE: 1 – 10

THURSDAY			
Energy	Sleep (hrs)	Sleep quality	Stress
Mood	Weather	Soreness	Weight
Injury/illness			

Ride 1	Ride 2
Resting heart rate:	Resting heart rate:
Route:	Route:
Distance:	Distance:
Time:	Time:
Zone: 1 2 3 4 5	Zone: 1 2 3 4 5
Average speed:	Average speed:
Max speed:	Max speed:
Inclination:	Inclination:
Food and water intake:	Food and water intake:
Ride report:	Ride report:
RPE: 1 – 10	RPE: 1 – 10

Week Beginning  / / Continued

FRIDAY			
Energy	Sleep (hrs)	Sleep quality	Stress
Mood	Weather	Soreness	Weight
Injury/illness			

Ride 1	Ride 2
Resting heart rate:	Resting heart rate:
Route:	Route:
Distance:	Distance:
Time:	Time:
Zone: 1 2 3 4 5	Zone: 1 2 3 4 5
Average speed:	Average speed:
Max speed:	Max speed:
Inclination:	Inclination:
Food and water intake:	Food and water intake:
Ride report:	Ride report:
RPE: 1 – 10	RPE: 1 – 10

SATURDAY			
Energy	Sleep (hrs)	Sleep quality	Stress
Mood	Weather	Soreness	Weight
Injury/illness			

Ride 1	Ride 2
Resting heart rate:	Resting heart rate:
Route:	Route:
Distance:	Distance:
Time:	Time:
Zone: 1 2 3 4 5	Zone: 1 2 3 4 5
Average speed:	Average speed:
Max speed:	Max speed:
Inclination:	Inclination:
Food and water intake:	Food and water intake:
Ride report:	Ride report:
RPE: 1 – 10	RPE: 1 – 10

SUNDAY			
Energy	Sleep (hrs)	Sleep quality	Stress
Mood	Weather	Soreness	Weight
Injury/illness			

Ride 1	Ride 2
Resting heart rate:	Resting heart rate:
Route:	Route:
Distance:	Distance:
Time:	Time:
Zone: 1 2 3 4 5	Zone: 1 2 3 4 5
Average speed:	Average speed:
Max speed:	Max speed:
Inclination:	Inclination:
Food and water intake:	Food and water intake:
Ride report:	Ride report:
RPE: 1 – 10	RPE: 1 – 10

WEEKLY COMPETITION	
Race 1	Race 2
Time Goal:	Time Goal:
Resting heart rate:	Resting heart rate:
Weather:	Weather:
Route:	Route:
Distance:	Distance:
Time:	Time:
Zone: 1 2 3 4 5	Zone: 1 2 3 4 5
Average speed:	Average speed:
Inclination:	Inclination:
Notes:	Notes:

WEEKLY SUMMARY			
Weight	Distance		Time
Average speed		RPE: 1 – 10	
Notes:			

Week Beginning

 / /

MONDAY

Energy		Sleep (hrs)		Sleep quality		Stress	
Mood		Weather		Soreness		Weight	

Injury/illness

Ride 1	Ride 2
Resting heart rate:	Resting heart rate:
Route:	Route:
Distance:	Distance:
Time:	Time:
Zone: 1 2 3 4 5	Zone: 1 2 3 4 5
Average speed:	Average speed:
Max speed:	Max speed:
Inclination:	Inclination:
Food and water intake:	Food and water intake:
Ride report:	Ride report:
RPE: 1 – 10	RPE: 1 – 10

TUESDAY

Energy		Sleep (hrs)		Sleep quality		Stress	
Mood		Weather		Soreness		Weight	

Injury/illness

Ride 1	Ride 2
Resting heart rate:	Resting heart rate:
Route:	Route:
Distance:	Distance:
Time:	Time:
Zone: 1 2 3 4 5	Zone: 1 2 3 4 5
Average speed:	Average speed:
Max speed:	Max speed:
Inclination:	Inclination:
Food and water intake:	Food and water intake:
Ride report:	Ride report:
RPE: 1 – 10	RPE: 1 – 10

Weekly Goals

WEDNESDAY			
Energy	Sleep (hrs)	Sleep quality	Stress
Mood	Weather	Soreness	Weight
Injury/illness			

Ride 1	Ride 2
Resting heart rate:	Resting heart rate:
Route:	Route:
Distance:	Distance:
Time:	Time:
Zone: 1 2 3 4 5	Zone: 1 2 3 4 5
Average speed:	Average speed:
Max speed:	Max speed:
Inclination:	Inclination:
Food and water intake:	Food and water intake:
Ride report:	Ride report:
RPE: 1 – 10	RPE: 1 – 10

THURSDAY			
Energy	Sleep (hrs)	Sleep quality	Stress
Mood	Weather	Soreness	Weight
Injury/illness			

Ride 1	Ride 2
Resting heart rate:	Resting heart rate:
Route:	Route:
Distance:	Distance:
Time:	Time:
Zone: 1 2 3 4 5	Zone: 1 2 3 4 5
Average speed:	Average speed:
Max speed:	Max speed:
Inclination:	Inclination:
Food and water intake:	Food and water intake:
Ride report:	Ride report:
RPE: 1 – 10	RPE: 1 – 10

FRIDAY			
Energy	Sleep (hrs)	Sleep quality	Stress
Mood	Weather	Soreness	Weight
Injury/illness			

Ride 1	Ride 2
Resting heart rate:	Resting heart rate:
Route:	Route:
Distance:	Distance:
Time:	Time:
Zone: 1 2 3 4 5	Zone: 1 2 3 4 5
Average speed:	Average speed:
Max speed:	Max speed:
Inclination:	Inclination:
Food and water intake:	Food and water intake:
Ride report:	Ride report:
RPE: 1 – 10	RPE: 1 – 10

SATURDAY			
Energy	Sleep (hrs)	Sleep quality	Stress
Mood	Weather	Soreness	Weight
Injury/illness			

Ride 1	Ride 2
Resting heart rate:	Resting heart rate:
Route:	Route:
Distance:	Distance:
Time:	Time:
Zone: 1 2 3 4 5	Zone: 1 2 3 4 5
Average speed:	Average speed:
Max speed:	Max speed:
Inclination:	Inclination:
Food and water intake:	Food and water intake:
Ride report:	Ride report:
RPE: 1 – 10	RPE: 1 – 10

SUNDAY			
Energy	Sleep (hrs)	Sleep quality	Stress
Mood	Weather	Soreness	Weight
Injury/illness			

Ride 1	Ride 2
Resting heart rate:	Resting heart rate:
Route:	Route:
Distance:	Distance:
Time:	Time:
Zone: 1 2 3 4 5	Zone: 1 2 3 4 5
Average speed:	Average speed:
Max speed:	Max speed:
Inclination:	Inclination:
Food and water intake:	Food and water intake:
Ride report:	Ride report:
RPE: 1 – 10	RPE: 1 – 10

WEEKLY COMPETITION	
Race 1	Race 2
Time Goal:	Time Goal:
Resting heart rate:	Resting heart rate:
Weather:	Weather:
Route:	Route:
Distance:	Distance:
Time:	Time:
Zone: 1 2 3 4 5	Zone: 1 2 3 4 5
Average speed:	Average speed:
Inclination:	Inclination:
Notes:	Notes:

WEEKLY SUMMARY		
Weight	Distance	Time
Average speed	RPE: 1 – 10	
Notes:		

Week Beginning

/   /

MONDAY			
Energy	Sleep (hrs)	Sleep quality	Stress
Mood	Weather	Soreness	Weight
Injury/illness			

Ride 1	Ride 2
Resting heart rate:	Resting heart rate:
Route:	Route:
Distance:	Distance:
Time:	Time:
Zone: 1 2 3 4 5	Zone: 1 2 3 4 5
Average speed:	Average speed:
Max speed:	Max speed:
Inclination:	Inclination:
Food and water intake:	Food and water intake:
Ride report:	Ride report:
RPE: 1 – 10	RPE: 1 – 10

TUESDAY			
Energy	Sleep (hrs)	Sleep quality	Stress
Mood	Weather	Soreness	Weight
Injury/illness			

Ride 1	Ride 2
Resting heart rate:	Resting heart rate:
Route:	Route:
Distance:	Distance:
Time:	Time:
Zone: 1 2 3 4 5	Zone: 1 2 3 4 5
Average speed:	Average speed:
Max speed:	Max speed:
Inclination:	Inclination:
Food and water intake:	Food and water intake:
Ride report:	Ride report:
RPE: 1 – 10	RPE: 1 – 10

Weekly Goals

WEDNESDAY			
Energy	Sleep (hrs)	Sleep quality	Stress
Mood	Weather	Soreness	Weight
Injury/illness			

Ride 1	Ride 2
Resting heart rate:	Resting heart rate:
Route:	Route:
Distance:	Distance:
Time:	Time:
Zone: 1 2 3 4 5	Zone: 1 2 3 4 5
Average speed:	Average speed:
Max speed:	Max speed:
Inclination:	Inclination:
Food and water intake:	Food and water intake:
Ride report:	Ride report:
RPE: 1 – 10	RPE: 1 – 10

THURSDAY			
Energy	Sleep (hrs)	Sleep quality	Stress
Mood	Weather	Soreness	Weight
Injury/illness			

Ride 1	Ride 2
Resting heart rate:	Resting heart rate:
Route:	Route:
Distance:	Distance:
Time:	Time:
Zone: 1 2 3 4 5	Zone: 1 2 3 4 5
Average speed:	Average speed:
Max speed:	Max speed:
Inclination:	Inclination:
Food and water intake:	Food and water intake:
Ride report:	Ride report:
RPE: 1 – 10	RPE: 1 – 10

FRIDAY			
Energy	Sleep (hrs)	Sleep quality	Stress
Mood	Weather	Soreness	Weight
Injury/illness			

Ride 1	Ride 2
Resting heart rate:	Resting heart rate:
Route:	Route:
Distance:	Distance:
Time:	Time:
Zone: 1 2 3 4 5	Zone: 1 2 3 4 5
Average speed:	Average speed:
Max speed:	Max speed:
Inclination:	Inclination:
Food and water intake:	Food and water intake:
Ride report:	Ride report:
RPE: 1 – 10	RPE: 1 – 10

SATURDAY			
Energy	Sleep (hrs)	Sleep quality	Stress
Mood	Weather	Soreness	Weight
Injury/illness			

Ride 1	Ride 2
Resting heart rate:	Resting heart rate:
Route:	Route:
Distance:	Distance:
Time:	Time:
Zone: 1 2 3 4 5	Zone: 1 2 3 4 5
Average speed:	Average speed:
Max speed:	Max speed:
Inclination:	Inclination:
Food and water intake:	Food and water intake:
Ride report:	Ride report:
RPE: 1 – 10	RPE: 1 – 10

SUNDAY			
Energy	Sleep (hrs)	Sleep quality	Stress
Mood	Weather	Soreness	Weight
Injury/illness			

Ride 1	Ride 2
Resting heart rate:	Resting heart rate:
Route:	Route:
Distance:	Distance:
Time:	Time:
Zone: 1 2 3 4 5	Zone: 1 2 3 4 5
Average speed:	Average speed:
Max speed:	Max speed:
Inclination:	Inclination:
Food and water intake:	Food and water intake:
Ride report:	Ride report:
RPE: 1 – 10	RPE: 1 – 10

WEEKLY COMPETITION	
Race 1	Race 2
Time Goal:	Time Goal:
Resting heart rate:	Resting heart rate:
Weather:	Weather:
Route:	Route:
Distance:	Distance:
Time:	Time:
Zone: 1 2 3 4 5	Zone: 1 2 3 4 5
Average speed:	Average speed:
Inclination:	Inclination:
Notes:	Notes:

WEEKLY SUMMARY		
Weight	Distance	Time
Average speed	RPE: 1 – 10	
Notes:		

Week Beginning

/ / /

MONDAY			
Energy	Sleep (hrs)	Sleep quality	Stress
Mood	Weather	Soreness	Weight
Injury/illness			

Ride 1	Ride 2
Resting heart rate:	Resting heart rate:
Route:	Route:
Distance:	Distance:
Time:	Time:
Zone: 1 2 3 4 5	Zone: 1 2 3 4 5
Average speed:	Average speed:
Max speed:	Max speed:
Inclination:	Inclination:
Food and water intake:	Food and water intake:
Ride report:	Ride report:
RPE: 1 – 10	RPE: 1 – 10

TUESDAY			
Energy	Sleep (hrs)	Sleep quality	Stress
Mood	Weather	Soreness	Weight
Injury/illness			

Ride 1	Ride 2
Resting heart rate:	Resting heart rate:
Route:	Route:
Distance:	Distance:
Time:	Time:
Zone: 1 2 3 4 5	Zone: 1 2 3 4 5
Average speed:	Average speed:
Max speed:	Max speed:
Inclination:	Inclination:
Food and water intake:	Food and water intake:
Ride report:	Ride report:
RPE: 1 – 10	RPE: 1 – 10

Weekly Goals

WEDNESDAY			
Energy	Sleep (hrs)	Sleep quality	Stress
Mood	Weather	Soreness	Weight
Injury/illness			

Ride 1		Ride 2	
Resting heart rate:		Resting heart rate:	
Route:		Route:	
Distance:		Distance:	
Time:		Time:	
Zone: 1 2 3 4 5		Zone: 1 2 3 4 5	
Average speed:		Average speed:	
Max speed:		Max speed:	
Inclination:		Inclination:	
Food and water intake:		Food and water intake:	
Ride report:		Ride report:	
RPE: 1 – 10		RPE: 1 – 10	

THURSDAY			
Energy	Sleep (hrs)	Sleep quality	Stress
Mood	Weather	Soreness	Weight
Injury/illness			

Ride 1		Ride 2	
Resting heart rate:		Resting heart rate:	
Route:		Route:	
Distance:		Distance:	
Time:		Time:	
Zone: 1 2 3 4 5		Zone: 1 2 3 4 5	
Average speed:		Average speed:	
Max speed:		Max speed:	
Inclination:		Inclination:	
Food and water intake:		Food and water intake:	
Ride report:		Ride report:	
RPE: 1 – 10		RPE: 1 – 10	

Week Beginning  / / Continued

FRIDAY			
Energy	Sleep (hrs)	Sleep quality	Stress
Mood	Weather	Soreness	Weight
Injury/illness			

Ride 1	Ride 2
Resting heart rate:	Resting heart rate:
Route:	Route:
Distance:	Distance:
Time:	Time:
Zone: 1 2 3 4 5	Zone: 1 2 3 4 5
Average speed:	Average speed:
Max speed:	Max speed:
Inclination:	Inclination:
Food and water intake:	Food and water intake:
Ride report:	Ride report:
RPE: 1 – 10	RPE: 1 – 10

SATURDAY			
Energy	Sleep (hrs)	Sleep quality	Stress
Mood	Weather	Soreness	Weight
Injury/illness			

Ride 1	Ride 2
Resting heart rate:	Resting heart rate:
Route:	Route:
Distance:	Distance:
Time:	Time:
Zone: 1 2 3 4 5	Zone: 1 2 3 4 5
Average speed:	Average speed:
Max speed:	Max speed:
Inclination:	Inclination:
Food and water intake:	Food and water intake:
Ride report:	Ride report:
RPE: 1 – 10	RPE: 1 – 10

SUNDAY			
Energy	Sleep (hrs)	Sleep quality	Stress
Mood	Weather	Soreness	Weight
Injury/illness			

Ride 1	Ride 2
Resting heart rate:	Resting heart rate:
Route:	Route:
Distance:	Distance:
Time:	Time:
Zone: 1 2 3 4 5	Zone: 1 2 3 4 5
Average speed:	Average speed:
Max speed:	Max speed:
Inclination:	Inclination:
Food and water intake:	Food and water intake:
Ride report:	Ride report:
RPE: 1 – 10	RPE: 1 – 10

WEEKLY COMPETITION	
Race 1	Race 2
Time Goal:	Time Goal:
Resting heart rate:	Resting heart rate:
Weather:	Weather:
Route:	Route:
Distance:	Distance:
Time:	Time:
Zone: 1 2 3 4 5	Zone: 1 2 3 4 5
Average speed:	Average speed:
Inclination:	Inclination:
Notes:	Notes:

WEEKLY SUMMARY			
Weight	Distance		Time
Average speed		RPE: 1 – 10	
Notes:			

Week Beginning

 / /

MONDAY			
Energy	Sleep (hrs)	Sleep quality	Stress
Mood	Weather	Soreness	Weight
Injury/illness			

Ride 1		Ride 2	
Resting heart rate:		Resting heart rate:	
Route:		Route:	
Distance:		Distance:	
Time:		Time:	
Zone: 1 2 3 4 5		Zone: 1 2 3 4 5	
Average speed:		Average speed:	
Max speed:		Max speed:	
Inclination:		Inclination:	
Food and water intake:		Food and water intake:	
Ride report:		Ride report:	
RPE: 1 – 10		RPE: 1 – 10	

TUESDAY			
Energy	Sleep (hrs)	Sleep quality	Stress
Mood	Weather	Soreness	Weight
Injury/illness			

Ride 1		Ride 2	
Resting heart rate:		Resting heart rate:	
Route:		Route:	
Distance:		Distance:	
Time:		Time:	
Zone: 1 2 3 4 5		Zone: 1 2 3 4 5	
Average speed:		Average speed:	
Max speed:		Max speed:	
Inclination:		Inclination:	
Food and water intake:		Food and water intake:	
Ride report:		Ride report:	
RPE: 1 – 10		RPE: 1 – 10	

Weekly Goals

WEDNESDAY			
Energy	Sleep (hrs)	Sleep quality	Stress
Mood	Weather	Soreness	Weight
Injury/illness			

Ride 1	Ride 2
Resting heart rate:	Resting heart rate:
Route:	Route:
Distance:	Distance:
Time:	Time:
Zone: 1 2 3 4 5	Zone: 1 2 3 4 5
Average speed:	Average speed:
Max speed:	Max speed:
Inclination:	Inclination:
Food and water intake:	Food and water intake:
Ride report:	Ride report:
RPE: 1 – 10	RPE: 1 – 10

THURSDAY			
Energy	Sleep (hrs)	Sleep quality	Stress
Mood	Weather	Soreness	Weight
Injury/illness			

Ride 1	Ride 2
Resting heart rate:	Resting heart rate:
Route:	Route:
Distance:	Distance:
Time:	Time:
Zone: 1 2 3 4 5	Zone: 1 2 3 4 5
Average speed:	Average speed:
Max speed:	Max speed:
Inclination:	Inclination:
Food and water intake:	Food and water intake:
Ride report:	Ride report:
RPE: 1 – 10	RPE: 1 – 10

Week Beginning / / Continued

FRIDAY			
Energy	Sleep (hrs)	Sleep quality	Stress
Mood	Weather	Soreness	Weight
Injury/illness			

Ride 1	Ride 2
Resting heart rate:	Resting heart rate:
Route:	Route:
Distance:	Distance:
Time:	Time:
Zone: 1 2 3 4 5	Zone: 1 2 3 4 5
Average speed:	Average speed:
Max speed:	Max speed:
Inclination:	Inclination:
Food and water intake:	Food and water intake:
Ride report:	Ride report:
RPE: 1 – 10	RPE: 1 – 10

SATURDAY			
Energy	Sleep (hrs)	Sleep quality	Stress
Mood	Weather	Soreness	Weight
Injury/illness			

Ride 1	Ride 2
Resting heart rate:	Resting heart rate:
Route:	Route:
Distance:	Distance:
Time:	Time:
Zone: 1 2 3 4 5	Zone: 1 2 3 4 5
Average speed:	Average speed:
Max speed:	Max speed:
Inclination:	Inclination:
Food and water intake:	Food and water intake:
Ride report:	Ride report:
RPE: 1 – 10	RPE: 1 – 10

SUNDAY			
Energy	Sleep (hrs)	Sleep quality	Stress
Mood	Weather	Soreness	Weight
Injury/illness			

Ride 1	Ride 2
Resting heart rate:	Resting heart rate:
Route:	Route:
Distance:	Distance:
Time:	Time:
Zone: 1 2 3 4 5	Zone: 1 2 3 4 5
Average speed:	Average speed:
Max speed:	Max speed:
Inclination:	Inclination:
Food and water intake:	Food and water intake:
Ride report:	Ride report:
RPE: 1 – 10	RPE: 1 – 10

WEEKLY COMPETITION	
Race 1	Race 2
Time Goal:	Time Goal:
Resting heart rate:	Resting heart rate:
Weather:	Weather:
Route:	Route:
Distance:	Distance:
Time:	Time:
Zone: 1 2 3 4 5	Zone: 1 2 3 4 5
Average speed:	Average speed:
Inclination:	Inclination:
Notes:	Notes:

WEEKLY SUMMARY		
Weight	Distance	Time
Average speed	RPE: 1 – 10	
Notes:		

Week Beginning

 / /

MONDAY			
Energy	Sleep (hrs)	Sleep quality	Stress
Mood	Weather	Soreness	Weight
Injury/illness			

Ride 1	Ride 2
Resting heart rate:	Resting heart rate:
Route:	Route:
Distance:	Distance:
Time:	Time:
Zone: 1 2 3 4 5	Zone: 1 2 3 4 5
Average speed:	Average speed:
Max speed:	Max speed:
Inclination:	Inclination:
Food and water intake:	Food and water intake:
Ride report:	Ride report:
RPE: 1 – 10	RPE: 1 – 10

TUESDAY			
Energy	Sleep (hrs)	Sleep quality	Stress
Mood	Weather	Soreness	Weight
Injury/illness			

Ride 1	Ride 2
Resting heart rate:	Resting heart rate:
Route:	Route:
Distance:	Distance:
Time:	Time:
Zone: 1 2 3 4 5	Zone: 1 2 3 4 5
Average speed:	Average speed:
Max speed:	Max speed:
Inclination:	Inclination:
Food and water intake:	Food and water intake:
Ride report:	Ride report:
RPE: 1 – 10	RPE: 1 – 10

Weekly Goals

WEDNESDAY			
Energy	Sleep (hrs)	Sleep quality	Stress
Mood	Weather	Soreness	Weight
Injury/illness			

Ride 1	Ride 2
Resting heart rate:	Resting heart rate:
Route:	Route:
Distance:	Distance:
Time:	Time:
Zone: 1 2 3 4 5	Zone: 1 2 3 4 5
Average speed:	Average speed:
Max speed:	Max speed:
Inclination:	Inclination:
Food and water intake:	Food and water intake:
Ride report:	Ride report:
RPE: 1 – 10	RPE: 1 – 10

THURSDAY			
Energy	Sleep (hrs)	Sleep quality	Stress
Mood	Weather	Soreness	Weight
Injury/illness			

Ride 1	Ride 2
Resting heart rate:	Resting heart rate:
Route:	Route:
Distance:	Distance:
Time:	Time:
Zone: 1 2 3 4 5	Zone: 1 2 3 4 5
Average speed:	Average speed:
Max speed:	Max speed:
Inclination:	Inclination:
Food and water intake:	Food and water intake:
Ride report:	Ride report:
RPE: 1 – 10	RPE: 1 – 10

FRIDAY			
Energy	Sleep (hrs)	Sleep quality	Stress
Mood	Weather	Soreness	Weight
Injury/illness			

Ride 1	Ride 2
Resting heart rate:	Resting heart rate:
Route:	Route:
Distance:	Distance:
Time:	Time:
Zone: 1 2 3 4 5	Zone: 1 2 3 4 5
Average speed:	Average speed:
Max speed:	Max speed:
Inclination:	Inclination:
Food and water intake:	Food and water intake:
Ride report:	Ride report:
RPE: 1 – 10	RPE: 1 – 10

SATURDAY			
Energy	Sleep (hrs)	Sleep quality	Stress
Mood	Weather	Soreness	Weight
Injury/illness			

Ride 1	Ride 2
Resting heart rate:	Resting heart rate:
Route:	Route:
Distance:	Distance:
Time:	Time:
Zone: 1 2 3 4 5	Zone: 1 2 3 4 5
Average speed:	Average speed:
Max speed:	Max speed:
Inclination:	Inclination:
Food and water intake:	Food and water intake:
Ride report:	Ride report:
RPE: 1 – 10	RPE: 1 – 10

SUNDAY			
Energy	Sleep (hrs)	Sleep quality	Stress
Mood	Weather	Soreness	Weight
Injury/illness			

Ride 1	Ride 2
Resting heart rate:	Resting heart rate:
Route:	Route:
Distance:	Distance:
Time:	Time:
Zone: 1 2 3 4 5	Zone: 1 2 3 4 5
Average speed:	Average speed:
Max speed:	Max speed:
Inclination:	Inclination:
Food and water intake:	Food and water intake:
Ride report:	Ride report:
RPE: 1 – 10	RPE: 1 – 10

WEEKLY COMPETITION	
Race 1	Race 2
Time Goal:	Time Goal:
Resting heart rate:	Resting heart rate:
Weather:	Weather:
Route:	Route:
Distance:	Distance:
Time:	Time:
Zone: 1 2 3 4 5	Zone: 1 2 3 4 5
Average speed:	Average speed:
Inclination:	Inclination:
Notes:	Notes:

WEEKLY SUMMARY		
Weight	Distance	Time
Average speed	RPE: 1 – 10	
Notes:		

Week Beginning

   /   /

MONDAY			
Energy	Sleep (hrs)	Sleep quality	Stress
Mood	Weather	Soreness	Weight
Injury/illness			

Ride 1	Ride 2
Resting heart rate:	Resting heart rate:
Route:	Route:
Distance:	Distance:
Time:	Time:
Zone: 1 2 3 4 5	Zone: 1 2 3 4 5
Average speed:	Average speed:
Max speed:	Max speed:
Inclination:	Inclination:
Food and water intake:	Food and water intake:
Ride report:	Ride report:
RPE: 1 – 10	RPE: 1 – 10

TUESDAY			
Energy	Sleep (hrs)	Sleep quality	Stress
Mood	Weather	Soreness	Weight
Injury/illness			

Ride 1	Ride 2
Resting heart rate:	Resting heart rate:
Route:	Route:
Distance:	Distance:
Time:	Time:
Zone: 1 2 3 4 5	Zone: 1 2 3 4 5
Average speed:	Average speed:
Max speed:	Max speed:
Inclination:	Inclination:
Food and water intake:	Food and water intake:
Ride report:	Ride report:
RPE: 1 – 10	RPE: 1 – 10

Weekly Goals

WEDNESDAY			
Energy	Sleep (hrs)	Sleep quality	Stress
Mood	Weather	Soreness	Weight
Injury/illness			

Ride 1	Ride 2
Resting heart rate:	Resting heart rate:
Route:	Route:
Distance:	Distance:
Time:	Time:
Zone: 1 2 3 4 5	Zone: 1 2 3 4 5
Average speed:	Average speed:
Max speed:	Max speed:
Inclination:	Inclination:
Food and water intake:	Food and water intake:
Ride report:	Ride report:
RPE: 1 – 10	RPE: 1 – 10

THURSDAY			
Energy	Sleep (hrs)	Sleep quality	Stress
Mood	Weather	Soreness	Weight
Injury/illness			

Ride 1	Ride 2
Resting heart rate:	Resting heart rate:
Route:	Route:
Distance:	Distance:
Time:	Time:
Zone: 1 2 3 4 5	Zone: 1 2 3 4 5
Average speed:	Average speed:
Max speed:	Max speed:
Inclination:	Inclination:
Food and water intake:	Food and water intake:
Ride report:	Ride report:
RPE: 1 – 10	RPE: 1 – 10

FRIDAY			
Energy	Sleep (hrs)	Sleep quality	Stress
Mood	Weather	Soreness	Weight
Injury/illness			

Ride 1	Ride 2
Resting heart rate:	Resting heart rate:
Route:	Route:
Distance:	Distance:
Time:	Time:
Zone: 1 2 3 4 5	Zone: 1 2 3 4 5
Average speed:	Average speed:
Max speed:	Max speed:
Inclination:	Inclination:
Food and water intake:	Food and water intake:
Ride report:	Ride report:
RPE: 1 – 10	RPE: 1 – 10

SATURDAY			
Energy	Sleep (hrs)	Sleep quality	Stress
Mood	Weather	Soreness	Weight
Injury/illness			

Ride 1	Ride 2
Resting heart rate:	Resting heart rate:
Route:	Route:
Distance:	Distance:
Time:	Time:
Zone: 1 2 3 4 5	Zone: 1 2 3 4 5
Average speed:	Average speed:
Max speed:	Max speed:
Inclination:	Inclination:
Food and water intake:	Food and water intake:
Ride report:	Ride report:
RPE: 1 – 10	RPE: 1 – 10

SUNDAY			
Energy	Sleep (hrs)	Sleep quality	Stress
Mood	Weather	Soreness	Weight
Injury/illness			

Ride 1	Ride 2
Resting heart rate:	Resting heart rate:
Route:	Route:
Distance:	Distance:
Time:	Time:
Zone: 1 2 3 4 5	Zone: 1 2 3 4 5
Average speed:	Average speed:
Max speed:	Max speed:
Inclination:	Inclination:
Food and water intake:	Food and water intake:
Ride report:	Ride report:
RPE: 1 – 10	RPE: 1 – 10

WEEKLY COMPETITION	
Race 1	Race 2
Time Goal:	Time Goal:
Resting heart rate:	Resting heart rate:
Weather:	Weather:
Route:	Route:
Distance:	Distance:
Time:	Time:
Zone: 1 2 3 4 5	Zone: 1 2 3 4 5
Average speed:	Average speed:
Inclination:	Inclination:
Notes:	Notes:

WEEKLY SUMMARY		
Weight	Distance	Time
Average speed	RPE: 1 – 10	
Notes:		

Week Beginning

 / /

MONDAY			
Energy	Sleep (hrs)	Sleep quality	Stress
Mood	Weather	Soreness	Weight
Injury/illness			

Ride 1	Ride 2
Resting heart rate:	Resting heart rate:
Route:	Route:
Distance:	Distance:
Time:	Time:
Zone: 1 2 3 4 5	Zone: 1 2 3 4 5
Average speed:	Average speed:
Max speed:	Max speed:
Inclination:	Inclination:
Food and water intake:	Food and water intake:
Ride report:	Ride report:
RPE: 1 – 10	RPE: 1 – 10

TUESDAY			
Energy	Sleep (hrs)	Sleep quality	Stress
Mood	Weather	Soreness	Weight
Injury/illness			

Ride 1	Ride 2
Resting heart rate:	Resting heart rate:
Route:	Route:
Distance:	Distance:
Time:	Time:
Zone: 1 2 3 4 5	Zone: 1 2 3 4 5
Average speed:	Average speed:
Max speed:	Max speed:
Inclination:	Inclination:
Food and water intake:	Food and water intake:
Ride report:	Ride report:
RPE: 1 – 10	RPE: 1 – 10

Weekly Goals

WEDNESDAY			
Energy	Sleep (hrs)	Sleep quality	Stress
Mood	Weather	Soreness	Weight
Injury/illness			

Ride 1	Ride 2
Resting heart rate:	Resting heart rate:
Route:	Route:
Distance:	Distance:
Time:	Time:
Zone: 1 2 3 4 5	Zone: 1 2 3 4 5
Average speed:	Average speed:
Max speed:	Max speed:
Inclination:	Inclination:
Food and water intake:	Food and water intake:
Ride report:	Ride report:
RPE: 1 – 10	RPE: 1 – 10

THURSDAY			
Energy	Sleep (hrs)	Sleep quality	Stress
Mood	Weather	Soreness	Weight
Injury/illness			

Ride 1	Ride 2
Resting heart rate:	Resting heart rate:
Route:	Route:
Distance:	Distance:
Time:	Time:
Zone: 1 2 3 4 5	Zone: 1 2 3 4 5
Average speed:	Average speed:
Max speed:	Max speed:
Inclination:	Inclination:
Food and water intake:	Food and water intake:
Ride report:	Ride report:
RPE: 1 – 10	RPE: 1 – 10

FRIDAY			
Energy	Sleep (hrs)	Sleep quality	Stress
Mood	Weather	Soreness	Weight
Injury/illness			

Ride 1		Ride 2	
Resting heart rate:		Resting heart rate:	
Route:		Route:	
Distance:		Distance:	
Time:		Time:	
Zone: 1 2 3 4 5		Zone: 1 2 3 4 5	
Average speed:		Average speed:	
Max speed:		Max speed:	
Inclination:		Inclination:	
Food and water intake:		Food and water intake:	
Ride report:		Ride report:	
RPE: 1 – 10		RPE: 1 – 10	

SATURDAY			
Energy	Sleep (hrs)	Sleep quality	Stress
Mood	Weather	Soreness	Weight
Injury/illness			

Ride 1		Ride 2	
Resting heart rate:		Resting heart rate:	
Route:		Route:	
Distance:		Distance:	
Time:		Time:	
Zone: 1 2 3 4 5		Zone: 1 2 3 4 5	
Average speed:		Average speed:	
Max speed:		Max speed:	
Inclination:		Inclination:	
Food and water intake:		Food and water intake:	
Ride report:		Ride report:	
RPE: 1 – 10		RPE: 1 – 10	

SUNDAY			
Energy	Sleep (hrs)	Sleep quality	Stress
Mood	Weather	Soreness	Weight
Injury/illness			

Ride 1	Ride 2
Resting heart rate:	Resting heart rate:
Route:	Route:
Distance:	Distance:
Time:	Time:
Zone: 1 2 3 4 5	Zone: 1 2 3 4 5
Average speed:	Average speed:
Max speed:	Max speed:
Inclination:	Inclination:
Food and water intake:	Food and water intake:
Ride report:	Ride report:
RPE: 1 – 10	RPE: 1 – 10

WEEKLY COMPETITION	
Race 1	Race 2
Time Goal:	Time Goal:
Resting heart rate:	Resting heart rate:
Weather:	Weather:
Route:	Route:
Distance:	Distance:
Time:	Time:
Zone: 1 2 3 4 5	Zone: 1 2 3 4 5
Average speed:	Average speed:
Inclination:	Inclination:
Notes:	Notes:

WEEKLY SUMMARY			
Weight	Distance		Time
Average speed		RPE: 1 – 10	
Notes:			

Week Beginning

 / /

MONDAY			
Energy	Sleep (hrs)	Sleep quality	Stress
Mood	Weather	Soreness	Weight
Injury/illness			

Ride 1	Ride 2
Resting heart rate:	Resting heart rate:
Route:	Route:
Distance:	Distance:
Time:	Time:
Zone: 1 2 3 4 5	Zone: 1 2 3 4 5
Average speed:	Average speed:
Max speed:	Max speed:
Inclination:	Inclination:
Food and water intake:	Food and water intake:
Ride report:	Ride report:
RPE: 1 – 10	RPE: 1 – 10

TUESDAY			
Energy	Sleep (hrs)	Sleep quality	Stress
Mood	Weather	Soreness	Weight
Injury/illness			

Ride 1	Ride 2
Resting heart rate:	Resting heart rate:
Route:	Route:
Distance:	Distance:
Time:	Time:
Zone: 1 2 3 4 5	Zone: 1 2 3 4 5
Average speed:	Average speed:
Max speed:	Max speed:
Inclination:	Inclination:
Food and water intake:	Food and water intake:
Ride report:	Ride report:
RPE: 1 – 10	RPE: 1 – 10

Weekly Goals

WEDNESDAY			
Energy	Sleep (hrs)	Sleep quality	Stress
Mood	Weather	Soreness	Weight
Injury/illness			

Ride 1	Ride 2
Resting heart rate:	Resting heart rate:
Route:	Route:
Distance:	Distance:
Time:	Time:
Zone: 1 2 3 4 5	Zone: 1 2 3 4 5
Average speed:	Average speed:
Max speed:	Max speed:
Inclination:	Inclination:
Food and water intake:	Food and water intake:
Ride report:	Ride report:
RPE: 1 – 10	RPE: 1 – 10

THURSDAY			
Energy	Sleep (hrs)	Sleep quality	Stress
Mood	Weather	Soreness	Weight
Injury/illness			

Ride 1	Ride 2
Resting heart rate:	Resting heart rate:
Route:	Route:
Distance:	Distance:
Time:	Time:
Zone: 1 2 3 4 5	Zone: 1 2 3 4 5
Average speed:	Average speed:
Max speed:	Max speed:
Inclination:	Inclination:
Food and water intake:	Food and water intake:
Ride report:	Ride report:
RPE: 1 – 10	RPE: 1 – 10

FRIDAY			
Energy	Sleep (hrs)	Sleep quality	Stress
Mood	Weather	Soreness	Weight
Injury/illness			

Ride 1	Ride 2
Resting heart rate:	Resting heart rate:
Route:	Route:
Distance:	Distance:
Time:	Time:
Zone: 1 2 3 4 5	Zone: 1 2 3 4 5
Average speed:	Average speed:
Max speed:	Max speed:
Inclination:	Inclination:
Food and water intake:	Food and water intake:
Ride report:	Ride report:
RPE: 1 – 10	RPE: 1 – 10

SATURDAY			
Energy	Sleep (hrs)	Sleep quality	Stress
Mood	Weather	Soreness	Weight
Injury/illness			

Ride 1	Ride 2
Resting heart rate:	Resting heart rate:
Route:	Route:
Distance:	Distance:
Time:	Time:
Zone: 1 2 3 4 5	Zone: 1 2 3 4 5
Average speed:	Average speed:
Max speed:	Max speed:
Inclination:	Inclination:
Food and water intake:	Food and water intake:
Ride report:	Ride report:
RPE: 1 – 10	RPE: 1 – 10

SUNDAY							
Energy		Sleep (hrs)		Sleep quality		Stress	
Mood		Weather		Soreness		Weight	
Injury/illness							

Ride 1					Ride 2				
Resting heart rate:					Resting heart rate:				
Route:					Route:				
Distance:					Distance:				
Time:					Time:				
Zone: 1	2	3	4	5	Zone: 1	2	3	4	5
Average speed:					Average speed:				
Max speed:					Max speed:				
Inclination:					Inclination:				
Food and water intake:					Food and water intake:				
Ride report:					Ride report:				
RPE: 1 – 10					RPE: 1 – 10				

WEEKLY COMPETITION									
Race 1					Race 2				
Time Goal:					Time Goal:				
Resting heart rate:					Resting heart rate:				
Weather:					Weather:				
Route:					Route:				
Distance:					Distance:				
Time:					Time:				
Zone: 1	2	3	4	5	Zone: 1	2	3	4	5
Average speed:					Average speed:				
Inclination:					Inclination:				
Notes:					Notes:				

WEEKLY SUMMARY			
Weight	Distance		Time
Average speed		RPE: 1 – 10	
Notes:			

Week Beginning

 / /

MONDAY			
Energy	Sleep (hrs)	Sleep quality	Stress
Mood	Weather	Soreness	Weight
Injury/illness			

Ride 1	Ride 2
Resting heart rate:	Resting heart rate:
Route:	Route:
Distance:	Distance:
Time:	Time:
Zone: 1 2 3 4 5	Zone: 1 2 3 4 5
Average speed:	Average speed:
Max speed:	Max speed:
Inclination:	Inclination:
Food and water intake:	Food and water intake:
Ride report:	Ride report:
RPE: 1 – 10	RPE: 1 – 10

TUESDAY			
Energy	Sleep (hrs)	Sleep quality	Stress
Mood	Weather	Soreness	Weight
Injury/illness			

Ride 1	Ride 2
Resting heart rate:	Resting heart rate:
Route:	Route:
Distance:	Distance:
Time:	Time:
Zone: 1 2 3 4 5	Zone: 1 2 3 4 5
Average speed:	Average speed:
Max speed:	Max speed:
Inclination:	Inclination:
Food and water intake:	Food and water intake:
Ride report:	Ride report:
RPE: 1 – 10	RPE: 1 – 10

Weekly Goals

WEDNESDAY			
Energy	Sleep (hrs)	Sleep quality	Stress
Mood	Weather	Soreness	Weight
Injury/illness			

Ride 1		Ride 2	
Resting heart rate:		Resting heart rate:	
Route:		Route:	
Distance:		Distance:	
Time:		Time:	
Zone: 1 2 3 4 5		Zone: 1 2 3 4 5	
Average speed:		Average speed:	
Max speed:		Max speed:	
Inclination:		Inclination:	
Food and water intake:		Food and water intake:	
Ride report:		Ride report:	
RPE: 1 – 10		RPE: 1 – 10	

THURSDAY			
Energy	Sleep (hrs)	Sleep quality	Stress
Mood	Weather	Soreness	Weight
Injury/illness			

Ride 1		Ride 2	
Resting heart rate:		Resting heart rate:	
Route:		Route:	
Distance:		Distance:	
Time:		Time:	
Zone: 1 2 3 4 5		Zone: 1 2 3 4 5	
Average speed:		Average speed:	
Max speed:		Max speed:	
Inclination:		Inclination:	
Food and water intake:		Food and water intake:	
Ride report:		Ride report:	
RPE: 1 – 10		RPE: 1 – 10	

Week Beginning  / / Continued

FRIDAY			
Energy	Sleep (hrs)	Sleep quality	Stress
Mood	Weather	Soreness	Weight
Injury/illness			

Ride 1	Ride 2
Resting heart rate:	Resting heart rate:
Route:	Route:
Distance:	Distance:
Time:	Time:
Zone: 1 2 3 4 5	Zone: 1 2 3 4 5
Average speed:	Average speed:
Max speed:	Max speed:
Inclination:	Inclination:
Food and water intake:	Food and water intake:
Ride report:	Ride report:
RPE: 1 – 10	RPE: 1 – 10

SATURDAY			
Energy	Sleep (hrs)	Sleep quality	Stress
Mood	Weather	Soreness	Weight
Injury/illness			

Ride 1	Ride 2
Resting heart rate:	Resting heart rate:
Route:	Route:
Distance:	Distance:
Time:	Time:
Zone: 1 2 3 4 5	Zone: 1 2 3 4 5
Average speed:	Average speed:
Max speed:	Max speed:
Inclination:	Inclination:
Food and water intake:	Food and water intake:
Ride report:	Ride report:
RPE: 1 – 10	RPE: 1 – 10

SUNDAY			
Energy	Sleep (hrs)	Sleep quality	Stress
Mood	Weather	Soreness	Weight
Injury/illness			

Ride 1	Ride 2
Resting heart rate:	Resting heart rate:
Route:	Route:
Distance:	Distance:
Time:	Time:
Zone: 1 2 3 4 5	Zone: 1 2 3 4 5
Average speed:	Average speed:
Max speed:	Max speed:
Inclination:	Inclination:
Food and water intake:	Food and water intake:
Ride report:	Ride report:
RPE: 1 – 10	RPE: 1 – 10

WEEKLY COMPETITION	
Race 1	Race 2
Time Goal:	Time Goal:
Resting heart rate:	Resting heart rate:
Weather:	Weather:
Route:	Route:
Distance:	Distance:
Time:	Time:
Zone: 1 2 3 4 5	Zone: 1 2 3 4 5
Average speed:	Average speed:
Inclination:	Inclination:
Notes:	Notes:

WEEKLY SUMMARY		
Weight	Distance	Time
Average speed	RPE: 1 – 10	
Notes:		

Week Beginning

 / /

MONDAY			
Energy	Sleep (hrs)	Sleep quality	Stress
Mood	Weather	Soreness	Weight
Injury/illness			

Ride 1	Ride 2
Resting heart rate:	Resting heart rate:
Route:	Route:
Distance:	Distance:
Time:	Time:
Zone: 1 2 3 4 5	Zone: 1 2 3 4 5
Average speed:	Average speed:
Max speed:	Max speed:
Inclination:	Inclination:
Food and water intake:	Food and water intake:
Ride report:	Ride report:
RPE: 1 – 10	RPE: 1 – 10

TUESDAY			
Energy	Sleep (hrs)	Sleep quality	Stress
Mood	Weather	Soreness	Weight
Injury/illness			

Ride 1	Ride 2
Resting heart rate:	Resting heart rate:
Route:	Route:
Distance:	Distance:
Time:	Time:
Zone: 1 2 3 4 5	Zone: 1 2 3 4 5
Average speed:	Average speed:
Max speed:	Max speed:
Inclination:	Inclination:
Food and water intake:	Food and water intake:
Ride report:	Ride report:
RPE: 1 – 10	RPE: 1 – 10

Weekly Goals

WEDNESDAY			
Energy	Sleep (hrs)	Sleep quality	Stress
Mood	Weather	Soreness	Weight
Injury/illness			

Ride 1	Ride 2
Resting heart rate:	Resting heart rate:
Route:	Route:
Distance:	Distance:
Time:	Time:
Zone: 1 2 3 4 5	Zone: 1 2 3 4 5
Average speed:	Average speed:
Max speed:	Max speed:
Inclination:	Inclination:
Food and water intake:	Food and water intake:
Ride report:	Ride report:
RPE: 1 – 10	RPE: 1 – 10

THURSDAY			
Energy	Sleep (hrs)	Sleep quality	Stress
Mood	Weather	Soreness	Weight
Injury/illness			

Ride 1	Ride 2
Resting heart rate:	Resting heart rate:
Route:	Route:
Distance:	Distance:
Time:	Time:
Zone: 1 2 3 4 5	Zone: 1 2 3 4 5
Average speed:	Average speed:
Max speed:	Max speed:
Inclination:	Inclination:
Food and water intake:	Food and water intake:
Ride report:	Ride report:
RPE: 1 – 10	RPE: 1 – 10

Week Beginning / / Continued

FRIDAY			
Energy	Sleep (hrs)	Sleep quality	Stress
Mood	Weather	Soreness	Weight
Injury/illness			

Ride 1	Ride 2
Resting heart rate:	Resting heart rate:
Route:	Route:
Distance:	Distance:
Time:	Time:
Zone: 1 2 3 4 5	Zone: 1 2 3 4 5
Average speed:	Average speed:
Max speed:	Max speed:
Inclination:	Inclination:
Food and water intake:	Food and water intake:
Ride report:	Ride report:
RPE: 1 – 10	RPE: 1 – 10

SATURDAY			
Energy	Sleep (hrs)	Sleep quality	Stress
Mood	Weather	Soreness	Weight
Injury/illness			

Ride 1	Ride 2
Resting heart rate:	Resting heart rate:
Route:	Route:
Distance:	Distance:
Time:	Time:
Zone: 1 2 3 4 5	Zone: 1 2 3 4 5
Average speed:	Average speed:
Max speed:	Max speed:
Inclination:	Inclination:
Food and water intake:	Food and water intake:
Ride report:	Ride report:
RPE: 1 – 10	RPE: 1 – 10

SUNDAY			
Energy	Sleep (hrs)	Sleep quality	Stress
Mood	Weather	Soreness	Weight
Injury/illness			

Ride 1	Ride 2
Resting heart rate:	Resting heart rate:
Route:	Route:
Distance:	Distance:
Time:	Time:
Zone: 1 2 3 4 5	Zone: 1 2 3 4 5
Average speed:	Average speed:
Max speed:	Max speed:
Inclination:	Inclination:
Food and water intake:	Food and water intake:
Ride report:	Ride report:
RPE: 1 – 10	RPE: 1 – 10

WEEKLY COMPETITION	
Race 1	Race 2
Time Goal:	Time Goal:
Resting heart rate:	Resting heart rate:
Weather:	Weather:
Route:	Route:
Distance:	Distance:
Time:	Time:
Zone: 1 2 3 4 5	Zone: 1 2 3 4 5
Average speed:	Average speed:
Inclination:	Inclination:
Notes:	Notes:

WEEKLY SUMMARY		
Weight	Distance	Time
Average speed	RPE: 1 – 10	
Notes:		

Week Beginning

 / /

MONDAY			
Energy	Sleep (hrs)	Sleep quality	Stress
Mood	Weather	Soreness	Weight
Injury/illness			

Ride 1		Ride 2	
Resting heart rate:		Resting heart rate:	
Route:		Route:	
Distance:		Distance:	
Time:		Time:	
Zone: 1 2 3 4 5		Zone: 1 2 3 4 5	
Average speed:		Average speed:	
Max speed:		Max speed:	
Inclination:		Inclination:	
Food and water intake:		Food and water intake:	
Ride report:		Ride report:	
RPE: 1 – 10		RPE: 1 – 10	

TUESDAY			
Energy	Sleep (hrs)	Sleep quality	Stress
Mood	Weather	Soreness	Weight
Injury/illness			

Ride 1		Ride 2	
Resting heart rate:		Resting heart rate:	
Route:		Route:	
Distance:		Distance:	
Time:		Time:	
Zone: 1 2 3 4 5		Zone: 1 2 3 4 5	
Average speed:		Average speed:	
Max speed:		Max speed:	
Inclination:		Inclination:	
Food and water intake:		Food and water intake:	
Ride report:		Ride report:	
RPE: 1 – 10		RPE: 1 – 10	

Weekly Goals

WEDNESDAY			
Energy	Sleep (hrs)	Sleep quality	Stress
Mood	Weather	Soreness	Weight
Injury/illness			

Ride 1	Ride 2
Resting heart rate:	Resting heart rate:
Route:	Route:
Distance:	Distance:
Time:	Time:
Zone: 1 2 3 4 5	Zone: 1 2 3 4 5
Average speed:	Average speed:
Max speed:	Max speed:
Inclination:	Inclination:
Food and water intake:	Food and water intake:
Ride report:	Ride report:
RPE: 1 – 10	RPE: 1 – 10

THURSDAY			
Energy	Sleep (hrs)	Sleep quality	Stress
Mood	Weather	Soreness	Weight
Injury/illness			

Ride 1	Ride 2
Resting heart rate:	Resting heart rate:
Route:	Route:
Distance:	Distance:
Time:	Time:
Zone: 1 2 3 4 5	Zone: 1 2 3 4 5
Average speed:	Average speed:
Max speed:	Max speed:
Inclination:	Inclination:
Food and water intake:	Food and water intake:
Ride report:	Ride report:
RPE: 1 – 10	RPE: 1 – 10

FRIDAY			
Energy	Sleep (hrs)	Sleep quality	Stress
Mood	Weather	Soreness	Weight
Injury/illness			

Ride 1	Ride 2
Resting heart rate:	Resting heart rate:
Route:	Route:
Distance:	Distance:
Time:	Time:
Zone: 1 2 3 4 5	Zone: 1 2 3 4 5
Average speed:	Average speed:
Max speed:	Max speed:
Inclination:	Inclination:
Food and water intake:	Food and water intake:
Ride report:	Ride report:
RPE: 1 – 10	RPE: 1 – 10

SATURDAY			
Energy	Sleep (hrs)	Sleep quality	Stress
Mood	Weather	Soreness	Weight
Injury/illness			

Ride 1	Ride 2
Resting heart rate:	Resting heart rate:
Route:	Route:
Distance:	Distance:
Time:	Time:
Zone: 1 2 3 4 5	Zone: 1 2 3 4 5
Average speed:	Average speed:
Max speed:	Max speed:
Inclination:	Inclination:
Food and water intake:	Food and water intake:
Ride report:	Ride report:
RPE: 1 – 10	RPE: 1 – 10

SUNDAY			
Energy	Sleep (hrs)	Sleep quality	Stress
Mood	Weather	Soreness	Weight
Injury/illness			

Ride 1		Ride 2	
Resting heart rate:		Resting heart rate:	
Route:		Route:	
Distance:		Distance:	
Time:		Time:	
Zone: 1 2 3 4 5		Zone: 1 2 3 4 5	
Average speed:		Average speed:	
Max speed:		Max speed:	
Inclination:		Inclination:	
Food and water intake:		Food and water intake:	
Ride report:		Ride report:	
RPE: 1 – 10		RPE: 1 – 10	

WEEKLY COMPETITION	
Race 1	Race 2
Time Goal:	Time Goal:
Resting heart rate:	Resting heart rate:
Weather:	Weather:
Route:	Route:
Distance:	Distance:
Time:	Time:
Zone: 1 2 3 4 5	Zone: 1 2 3 4 5
Average speed:	Average speed:
Inclination:	Inclination:
Notes:	Notes:

WEEKLY SUMMARY			
Weight	Distance		Time
Average speed		RPE: 1 – 10	
Notes:			

Week Beginning

/ / /

MONDAY			
Energy	Sleep (hrs)	Sleep quality	Stress
Mood	Weather	Soreness	Weight
Injury/illness			

Ride 1	Ride 2
Resting heart rate:	Resting heart rate:
Route:	Route:
Distance:	Distance:
Time:	Time:
Zone: 1 2 3 4 5	Zone: 1 2 3 4 5
Average speed:	Average speed:
Max speed:	Max speed:
Inclination:	Inclination:
Food and water intake:	Food and water intake:
Ride report:	Ride report:
RPE: 1 – 10	RPE: 1 – 10

TUESDAY			
Energy	Sleep (hrs)	Sleep quality	Stress
Mood	Weather	Soreness	Weight
Injury/illness			

Ride 1	Ride 2
Resting heart rate:	Resting heart rate:
Route:	Route:
Distance:	Distance:
Time:	Time:
Zone: 1 2 3 4 5	Zone: 1 2 3 4 5
Average speed:	Average speed:
Max speed:	Max speed:
Inclination:	Inclination:
Food and water intake:	Food and water intake:
Ride report:	Ride report:
RPE: 1 – 10	RPE: 1 – 10

Weekly Goals

WEDNESDAY			
Energy	Sleep (hrs)	Sleep quality	Stress
Mood	Weather	Soreness	Weight
Injury/illness			

Ride 1	Ride 2
Resting heart rate:	Resting heart rate:
Route:	Route:
Distance:	Distance:
Time:	Time:
Zone: 1 2 3 4 5	Zone: 1 2 3 4 5
Average speed:	Average speed:
Max speed:	Max speed:
Inclination:	Inclination:
Food and water intake:	Food and water intake:
Ride report:	Ride report:
RPE: 1 – 10	RPE: 1 – 10

THURSDAY			
Energy	Sleep (hrs)	Sleep quality	Stress
Mood	Weather	Soreness	Weight
Injury/illness			

Ride 1	Ride 2
Resting heart rate:	Resting heart rate:
Route:	Route:
Distance:	Distance:
Time:	Time:
Zone: 1 2 3 4 5	Zone: 1 2 3 4 5
Average speed:	Average speed:
Max speed:	Max speed:
Inclination:	Inclination:
Food and water intake:	Food and water intake:
Ride report:	Ride report:
RPE: 1 – 10	RPE: 1 – 10

Week Beginning / / Continued

FRIDAY			
Energy	Sleep (hrs)	Sleep quality	Stress
Mood	Weather	Soreness	Weight
Injury/illness			

Ride 1	Ride 2
Resting heart rate:	Resting heart rate:
Route:	Route:
Distance:	Distance:
Time:	Time:
Zone: 1　　2　　3　　4　　5	Zone: 1　　2　　3　　4　　5
Average speed:	Average speed:
Max speed:	Max speed:
Inclination:	Inclination:
Food and water intake:	Food and water intake:
Ride report:	Ride report:
RPE: 1 – 10	RPE: 1 – 10

SATURDAY			
Energy	Sleep (hrs)	Sleep quality	Stress
Mood	Weather	Soreness	Weight
Injury/illness			

Ride 1	Ride 2
Resting heart rate:	Resting heart rate:
Route:	Route:
Distance:	Distance:
Time:	Time:
Zone: 1　　2　　3　　4　　5	Zone: 1　　2　　3　　4　　5
Average speed:	Average speed:
Max speed:	Max speed:
Inclination:	Inclination:
Food and water intake:	Food and water intake:
Ride report:	Ride report:
RPE: 1 – 10	RPE: 1 – 10

SUNDAY			
Energy	Sleep (hrs)	Sleep quality	Stress
Mood	Weather	Soreness	Weight
Injury/illness			

Ride 1	Ride 2
Resting heart rate:	Resting heart rate:
Route:	Route:
Distance:	Distance:
Time:	Time:
Zone: 1 2 3 4 5	Zone: 1 2 3 4 5
Average speed:	Average speed:
Max speed:	Max speed:
Inclination:	Inclination:
Food and water intake:	Food and water intake:
Ride report:	Ride report:
RPE: 1 – 10	RPE: 1 – 10

WEEKLY COMPETITION	
Race 1	Race 2
Time Goal:	Time Goal:
Resting heart rate:	Resting heart rate:
Weather:	Weather:
Route:	Route:
Distance:	Distance:
Time:	Time:
Zone: 1 2 3 4 5	Zone: 1 2 3 4 5
Average speed:	Average speed:
Inclination:	Inclination:
Notes:	Notes:

WEEKLY SUMMARY		
Weight	Distance	Time
Average speed	RPE: 1 – 10	
Notes:		

Week Beginning

 / /

MONDAY			
Energy	Sleep (hrs)	Sleep quality	Stress
Mood	Weather	Soreness	Weight
Injury/illness			

Ride 1	Ride 2
Resting heart rate:	Resting heart rate:
Route:	Route:
Distance:	Distance:
Time:	Time:
Zone: 1　2　3　4　5	Zone: 1　2　3　4　5
Average speed:	Average speed:
Max speed:	Max speed:
Inclination:	Inclination:
Food and water intake:	Food and water intake:
Ride report:	Ride report:
RPE: 1 – 10	RPE: 1 – 10

TUESDAY			
Energy	Sleep (hrs)	Sleep quality	Stress
Mood	Weather	Soreness	Weight
Injury/illness			

Ride 1	Ride 2
Resting heart rate:	Resting heart rate:
Route:	Route:
Distance:	Distance:
Time:	Time:
Zone: 1　2　3　4　5	Zone: 1　2　3　4　5
Average speed:	Average speed:
Max speed:	Max speed:
Inclination:	Inclination:
Food and water intake:	Food and water intake:
Ride report:	Ride report:
RPE: 1 – 10	RPE: 1 – 10

Weekly Goals

WEDNESDAY			
Energy	Sleep (hrs)	Sleep quality	Stress
Mood	Weather	Soreness	Weight
Injury/illness			

Ride 1	Ride 2
Resting heart rate:	Resting heart rate:
Route:	Route:
Distance:	Distance:
Time:	Time:
Zone: 1 2 3 4 5	Zone: 1 2 3 4 5
Average speed:	Average speed:
Max speed:	Max speed:
Inclination:	Inclination:
Food and water intake:	Food and water intake:
Ride report:	Ride report:
RPE: 1 – 10	RPE: 1 – 10

THURSDAY			
Energy	Sleep (hrs)	Sleep quality	Stress
Mood	Weather	Soreness	Weight
Injury/illness			

Ride 1	Ride 2
Resting heart rate:	Resting heart rate:
Route:	Route:
Distance:	Distance:
Time:	Time:
Zone: 1 2 3 4 5	Zone: 1 2 3 4 5
Average speed:	Average speed:
Max speed:	Max speed:
Inclination:	Inclination:
Food and water intake:	Food and water intake:
Ride report:	Ride report:
RPE: 1 – 10	RPE: 1 – 10

FRIDAY			
Energy	Sleep (hrs)	Sleep quality	Stress
Mood	Weather	Soreness	Weight
Injury/illness			

Ride 1	Ride 2
Resting heart rate:	Resting heart rate:
Route:	Route:
Distance:	Distance:
Time:	Time:
Zone: 1 2 3 4 5	Zone: 1 2 3 4 5
Average speed:	Average speed:
Max speed:	Max speed:
Inclination:	Inclination:
Food and water intake:	Food and water intake:
Ride report:	Ride report:
RPE: 1 – 10	RPE: 1 – 10

SATURDAY			
Energy	Sleep (hrs)	Sleep quality	Stress
Mood	Weather	Soreness	Weight
Injury/illness			

Ride 1	Ride 2
Resting heart rate:	Resting heart rate:
Route:	Route:
Distance:	Distance:
Time:	Time:
Zone: 1 2 3 4 5	Zone: 1 2 3 4 5
Average speed:	Average speed:
Max speed:	Max speed:
Inclination:	Inclination:
Food and water intake:	Food and water intake:
Ride report:	Ride report:
RPE: 1 – 10	RPE: 1 – 10

SUNDAY			
Energy	Sleep (hrs)	Sleep quality	Stress
Mood	Weather	Soreness	Weight
Injury/illness			

Ride 1	Ride 2
Resting heart rate:	Resting heart rate:
Route:	Route:
Distance:	Distance:
Time:	Time:
Zone: 1 2 3 4 5	Zone: 1 2 3 4 5
Average speed:	Average speed:
Max speed:	Max speed:
Inclination:	Inclination:
Food and water intake:	Food and water intake:
Ride report:	Ride report:
RPE: 1 – 10	RPE: 1 – 10

WEEKLY COMPETITION	
Race 1	Race 2
Time Goal:	Time Goal:
Resting heart rate:	Resting heart rate:
Weather:	Weather:
Route:	Route:
Distance:	Distance:
Time:	Time:
Zone: 1 2 3 4 5	Zone: 1 2 3 4 5
Average speed:	Average speed:
Inclination:	Inclination:
Notes:	Notes:

WEEKLY SUMMARY			
Weight	Distance		Time
Average speed		RPE: 1 – 10	
Notes:			

Week Beginning

/ /

MONDAY			
Energy	Sleep (hrs)	Sleep quality	Stress
Mood	Weather	Soreness	Weight
Injury/illness			

Ride 1	Ride 2
Resting heart rate:	Resting heart rate:
Route:	Route:
Distance:	Distance:
Time:	Time:
Zone: 1 2 3 4 5	Zone: 1 2 3 4 5
Average speed:	Average speed:
Max speed:	Max speed:
Inclination:	Inclination:
Food and water intake:	Food and water intake:
Ride report:	Ride report:
RPE: 1 – 10	RPE: 1 – 10

TUESDAY			
Energy	Sleep (hrs)	Sleep quality	Stress
Mood	Weather	Soreness	Weight
Injury/illness			

Ride 1	Ride 2
Resting heart rate:	Resting heart rate:
Route:	Route:
Distance:	Distance:
Time:	Time:
Zone: 1 2 3 4 5	Zone: 1 2 3 4 5
Average speed:	Average speed:
Max speed:	Max speed:
Inclination:	Inclination:
Food and water intake:	Food and water intake:
Ride report:	Ride report:
RPE: 1 – 10	RPE: 1 – 10

Weekly Goals

WEDNESDAY			
Energy	Sleep (hrs)	Sleep quality	Stress
Mood	Weather	Soreness	Weight
Injury/illness			

Ride 1	Ride 2
Resting heart rate:	Resting heart rate:
Route:	Route:
Distance:	Distance:
Time:	Time:
Zone: 1 2 3 4 5	Zone: 1 2 3 4 5
Average speed:	Average speed:
Max speed:	Max speed:
Inclination:	Inclination:
Food and water intake:	Food and water intake:
Ride report:	Ride report:
RPE: 1 – 10	RPE: 1 – 10

THURSDAY			
Energy	Sleep (hrs)	Sleep quality	Stress
Mood	Weather	Soreness	Weight
Injury/illness			

Ride 1	Ride 2
Resting heart rate:	Resting heart rate:
Route:	Route:
Distance:	Distance:
Time:	Time:
Zone: 1 2 3 4 5	Zone: 1 2 3 4 5
Average speed:	Average speed:
Max speed:	Max speed:
Inclination:	Inclination:
Food and water intake:	Food and water intake:
Ride report:	Ride report:
RPE: 1 – 10	RPE: 1 – 10

FRIDAY			
Energy	Sleep (hrs)	Sleep quality	Stress
Mood	Weather	Soreness	Weight
Injury/illness			

Ride 1	Ride 2
Resting heart rate:	Resting heart rate:
Route:	Route:
Distance:	Distance:
Time:	Time:
Zone: 1 2 3 4 5	Zone: 1 2 3 4 5
Average speed:	Average speed:
Max speed:	Max speed:
Inclination:	Inclination:
Food and water intake:	Food and water intake:
Ride report:	Ride report:
RPE: 1 – 10	RPE: 1 – 10

SATURDAY			
Energy	Sleep (hrs)	Sleep quality	Stress
Mood	Weather	Soreness	Weight
Injury/illness			

Ride 1	Ride 2
Resting heart rate:	Resting heart rate:
Route:	Route:
Distance:	Distance:
Time:	Time:
Zone: 1 2 3 4 5	Zone: 1 2 3 4 5
Average speed:	Average speed:
Max speed:	Max speed:
Inclination:	Inclination:
Food and water intake:	Food and water intake:
Ride report:	Ride report:
RPE: 1 – 10	RPE: 1 – 10

SUNDAY			
Energy	Sleep (hrs)	Sleep quality	Stress
Mood	Weather	Soreness	Weight
Injury/illness			

Ride 1	Ride 2
Resting heart rate:	Resting heart rate:
Route:	Route:
Distance:	Distance:
Time:	Time:
Zone: 1 2 3 4 5	Zone: 1 2 3 4 5
Average speed:	Average speed:
Max speed:	Max speed:
Inclination:	Inclination:
Food and water intake:	Food and water intake:
Ride report:	Ride report:
RPE: 1 – 10	RPE: 1 – 10

WEEKLY COMPETITION	
Race 1	Race 2
Time Goal:	Time Goal:
Resting heart rate:	Resting heart rate:
Weather:	Weather:
Route:	Route:
Distance:	Distance:
Time:	Time:
Zone: 1 2 3 4 5	Zone: 1 2 3 4 5
Average speed:	Average speed:
Inclination:	Inclination:
Notes:	Notes:

WEEKLY SUMMARY			
Weight	Distance		Time
Average speed		RPE: 1 – 10	
Notes:			

Week Beginning

 / /

MONDAY			
Energy	Sleep (hrs)	Sleep quality	Stress
Mood	Weather	Soreness	Weight
Injury/illness			

Ride 1	Ride 2
Resting heart rate:	Resting heart rate:
Route:	Route:
Distance:	Distance:
Time:	Time:
Zone: 1 2 3 4 5	Zone: 1 2 3 4 5
Average speed:	Average speed:
Max speed:	Max speed:
Inclination:	Inclination:
Food and water intake:	Food and water intake:
Ride report:	Ride report:
RPE: 1 – 10	RPE: 1 – 10

TUESDAY			
Energy	Sleep (hrs)	Sleep quality	Stress
Mood	Weather	Soreness	Weight
Injury/illness			

Ride 1	Ride 2
Resting heart rate:	Resting heart rate:
Route:	Route:
Distance:	Distance:
Time:	Time:
Zone: 1 2 3 4 5	Zone: 1 2 3 4 5
Average speed:	Average speed:
Max speed:	Max speed:
Inclination:	Inclination:
Food and water intake:	Food and water intake:
Ride report:	Ride report:
RPE: 1 – 10	RPE: 1 – 10

Weekly Goals

WEDNESDAY			
Energy	Sleep (hrs)	Sleep quality	Stress
Mood	Weather	Soreness	Weight
Injury/illness			

Ride 1	Ride 2
Resting heart rate:	Resting heart rate:
Route:	Route:
Distance:	Distance:
Time:	Time:
Zone: 1 2 3 4 5	Zone: 1 2 3 4 5
Average speed:	Average speed:
Max speed:	Max speed:
Inclination:	Inclination:
Food and water intake:	Food and water intake:
Ride report:	Ride report:
RPE: 1 – 10	RPE: 1 – 10

THURSDAY			
Energy	Sleep (hrs)	Sleep quality	Stress
Mood	Weather	Soreness	Weight
Injury/illness			

Ride 1	Ride 2
Resting heart rate:	Resting heart rate:
Route:	Route:
Distance:	Distance:
Time:	Time:
Zone: 1 2 3 4 5	Zone: 1 2 3 4 5
Average speed:	Average speed:
Max speed:	Max speed:
Inclination:	Inclination:
Food and water intake:	Food and water intake:
Ride report:	Ride report:
RPE: 1 – 10	RPE: 1 – 10

FRIDAY			
Energy	Sleep (hrs)	Sleep quality	Stress
Mood	Weather	Soreness	Weight
Injury/illness			

Ride 1		Ride 2	
Resting heart rate:		Resting heart rate:	
Route:		Route:	
Distance:		Distance:	
Time:		Time:	
Zone: 1 2 3 4 5		Zone: 1 2 3 4 5	
Average speed:		Average speed:	
Max speed:		Max speed:	
Inclination:		Inclination:	
Food and water intake:		Food and water intake:	
Ride report:		Ride report:	
RPE: 1 – 10		RPE: 1 – 10	

SATURDAY			
Energy	Sleep (hrs)	Sleep quality	Stress
Mood	Weather	Soreness	Weight
Injury/illness			

Ride 1		Ride 2	
Resting heart rate:		Resting heart rate:	
Route:		Route:	
Distance:		Distance:	
Time:		Time:	
Zone: 1 2 3 4 5		Zone: 1 2 3 4 5	
Average speed:		Average speed:	
Max speed:		Max speed:	
Inclination:		Inclination:	
Food and water intake:		Food and water intake:	
Ride report:		Ride report:	
RPE: 1 – 10		RPE: 1 – 10	

SUNDAY			
Energy	Sleep (hrs)	Sleep quality	Stress
Mood	Weather	Soreness	Weight
Injury/illness			

Ride 1	Ride 2
Resting heart rate:	Resting heart rate:
Route:	Route:
Distance:	Distance:
Time:	Time:
Zone: 1 2 3 4 5	Zone: 1 2 3 4 5
Average speed:	Average speed:
Max speed:	Max speed:
Inclination:	Inclination:
Food and water intake:	Food and water intake:
Ride report:	Ride report:
RPE: 1 – 10	RPE: 1 – 10

WEEKLY COMPETITION	
Race 1	Race 2
Time Goal:	Time Goal:
Resting heart rate:	Resting heart rate:
Weather:	Weather:
Route:	Route:
Distance:	Distance:
Time:	Time:
Zone: 1 2 3 4 5	Zone: 1 2 3 4 5
Average speed:	Average speed:
Inclination:	Inclination:
Notes:	Notes:

WEEKLY SUMMARY		
Weight	Distance	Time
Average speed	RPE: 1 – 10	
Notes:		

Week Beginning

 /   /

MONDAY			
Energy	Sleep (hrs)	Sleep quality	Stress
Mood	Weather	Soreness	Weight
Injury/illness			

Ride 1	Ride 2
Resting heart rate:	Resting heart rate:
Route:	Route:
Distance:	Distance:
Time:	Time:
Zone: 1 2 3 4 5	Zone: 1 2 3 4 5
Average speed:	Average speed:
Max speed:	Max speed:
Inclination:	Inclination:
Food and water intake:	Food and water intake:
Ride report:	Ride report:
RPE: 1 – 10	RPE: 1 – 10

TUESDAY			
Energy	Sleep (hrs)	Sleep quality	Stress
Mood	Weather	Soreness	Weight
Injury/illness			

Ride 1	Ride 2
Resting heart rate:	Resting heart rate:
Route:	Route:
Distance:	Distance:
Time:	Time:
Zone: 1 2 3 4 5	Zone: 1 2 3 4 5
Average speed:	Average speed:
Max speed:	Max speed:
Inclination:	Inclination:
Food and water intake:	Food and water intake:
Ride report:	Ride report:
RPE: 1 – 10	RPE: 1 – 10

Weekly Goals

WEDNESDAY			
Energy	Sleep (hrs)	Sleep quality	Stress
Mood	Weather	Soreness	Weight
Injury/illness			

Ride 1	Ride 2
Resting heart rate:	Resting heart rate:
Route:	Route:
Distance:	Distance:
Time:	Time:
Zone: 1 2 3 4 5	Zone: 1 2 3 4 5
Average speed:	Average speed:
Max speed:	Max speed:
Inclination:	Inclination:
Food and water intake:	Food and water intake:
Ride report:	Ride report:
RPE: 1 – 10	RPE: 1 – 10

THURSDAY			
Energy	Sleep (hrs)	Sleep quality	Stress
Mood	Weather	Soreness	Weight
Injury/illness			

Ride 1	Ride 2
Resting heart rate:	Resting heart rate:
Route:	Route:
Distance:	Distance:
Time:	Time:
Zone: 1 2 3 4 5	Zone: 1 2 3 4 5
Average speed:	Average speed:
Max speed:	Max speed:
Inclination:	Inclination:
Food and water intake:	Food and water intake:
Ride report:	Ride report:
RPE: 1 – 10	RPE: 1 – 10

FRIDAY			
Energy	Sleep (hrs)	Sleep quality	Stress
Mood	Weather	Soreness	Weight
Injury/illness			

Ride 1	Ride 2
Resting heart rate:	Resting heart rate:
Route:	Route:
Distance:	Distance:
Time:	Time:
Zone: 1 2 3 4 5	Zone: 1 2 3 4 5
Average speed:	Average speed:
Max speed:	Max speed:
Inclination:	Inclination:
Food and water intake:	Food and water intake:
Ride report:	Ride report:
RPE: 1 – 10	RPE: 1 – 10

SATURDAY			
Energy	Sleep (hrs)	Sleep quality	Stress
Mood	Weather	Soreness	Weight
Injury/illness			

Ride 1	Ride 2
Resting heart rate:	Resting heart rate:
Route:	Route:
Distance:	Distance:
Time:	Time:
Zone: 1 2 3 4 5	Zone: 1 2 3 4 5
Average speed:	Average speed:
Max speed:	Max speed:
Inclination:	Inclination:
Food and water intake:	Food and water intake:
Ride report:	Ride report:
RPE: 1 – 10	RPE: 1 – 10

SUNDAY			
Energy	Sleep (hrs)	Sleep quality	Stress
Mood	Weather	Soreness	Weight
Injury/illness			

Ride 1	Ride 2
Resting heart rate:	Resting heart rate:
Route:	Route:
Distance:	Distance:
Time:	Time:
Zone: 1 2 3 4 5	Zone: 1 2 3 4 5
Average speed:	Average speed:
Max speed:	Max speed:
Inclination:	Inclination:
Food and water intake:	Food and water intake:
Ride report:	Ride report:
RPE: 1 – 10	RPE: 1 – 10

WEEKLY COMPETITION	
Race 1	Race 2
Time Goal:	Time Goal:
Resting heart rate:	Resting heart rate:
Weather:	Weather:
Route:	Route:
Distance:	Distance:
Time:	Time:
Zone: 1 2 3 4 5	Zone: 1 2 3 4 5
Average speed:	Average speed:
Inclination:	Inclination:
Notes:	Notes:

WEEKLY SUMMARY			
Weight	Distance		Time
Average speed		RPE: 1 – 10	
Notes:			

Week Beginning

/ /

MONDAY			
Energy	Sleep (hrs)	Sleep quality	Stress
Mood	Weather	Soreness	Weight
Injury/illness			

Ride 1	Ride 2
Resting heart rate:	Resting heart rate:
Route:	Route:
Distance:	Distance:
Time:	Time:
Zone: 1 2 3 4 5	Zone: 1 2 3 4 5
Average speed:	Average speed:
Max speed:	Max speed:
Inclination:	Inclination:
Food and water intake:	Food and water intake:
Ride report:	Ride report:
RPE: 1 – 10	RPE: 1 – 10

TUESDAY			
Energy	Sleep (hrs)	Sleep quality	Stress
Mood	Weather	Soreness	Weight
Injury/illness			

Ride 1	Ride 2
Resting heart rate:	Resting heart rate:
Route:	Route:
Distance:	Distance:
Time:	Time:
Zone: 1 2 3 4 5	Zone: 1 2 3 4 5
Average speed:	Average speed:
Max speed:	Max speed:
Inclination:	Inclination:
Food and water intake:	Food and water intake:
Ride report:	Ride report:
RPE: 1 – 10	RPE: 1 – 10

Weekly Goals

WEDNESDAY			
Energy	Sleep (hrs)	Sleep quality	Stress
Mood	Weather	Soreness	Weight
Injury/illness			

Ride 1	Ride 2
Resting heart rate:	Resting heart rate:
Route:	Route:
Distance:	Distance:
Time:	Time:
Zone: 1 2 3 4 5	Zone: 1 2 3 4 5
Average speed:	Average speed:
Max speed:	Max speed:
Inclination:	Inclination:
Food and water intake:	Food and water intake:
Ride report:	Ride report:
RPE: 1 – 10	RPE: 1 – 10

THURSDAY			
Energy	Sleep (hrs)	Sleep quality	Stress
Mood	Weather	Soreness	Weight
Injury/illness			

Ride 1	Ride 2
Resting heart rate:	Resting heart rate:
Route:	Route:
Distance:	Distance:
Time:	Time:
Zone: 1 2 3 4 5	Zone: 1 2 3 4 5
Average speed:	Average speed:
Max speed:	Max speed:
Inclination:	Inclination:
Food and water intake:	Food and water intake:
Ride report:	Ride report:
RPE: 1 – 10	RPE: 1 – 10

Week Beginning Continued

FRIDAY			
Energy	Sleep (hrs)	Sleep quality	Stress
Mood	Weather	Soreness	Weight
Injury/illness			

Ride 1	Ride 2
Resting heart rate:	Resting heart rate:
Route:	Route:
Distance:	Distance:
Time:	Time:
Zone: 1 2 3 4 5	Zone: 1 2 3 4 5
Average speed:	Average speed:
Max speed:	Max speed:
Inclination:	Inclination:
Food and water intake:	Food and water intake:
Ride report:	Ride report:
RPE: 1 – 10	RPE: 1 – 10

SATURDAY			
Energy	Sleep (hrs)	Sleep quality	Stress
Mood	Weather	Soreness	Weight
Injury/illness			

Ride 1	Ride 2
Resting heart rate:	Resting heart rate:
Route:	Route:
Distance:	Distance:
Time:	Time:
Zone: 1 2 3 4 5	Zone: 1 2 3 4 5
Average speed:	Average speed:
Max speed:	Max speed:
Inclination:	Inclination:
Food and water intake:	Food and water intake:
Ride report:	Ride report:
RPE: 1 – 10	RPE: 1 – 10

SUNDAY			
Energy	Sleep (hrs)	Sleep quality	Stress
Mood	Weather	Soreness	Weight
Injury/illness			

Ride 1	Ride 2
Resting heart rate:	Resting heart rate:
Route:	Route:
Distance:	Distance:
Time:	Time:
Zone: 1 2 3 4 5	Zone: 1 2 3 4 5
Average speed:	Average speed:
Max speed:	Max speed:
Inclination:	Inclination:
Food and water intake:	Food and water intake:
Ride report:	Ride report:
RPE: 1 – 10	RPE: 1 – 10

WEEKLY COMPETITION	
Race 1	Race 2
Time Goal:	Time Goal:
Resting heart rate:	Resting heart rate:
Weather:	Weather:
Route:	Route:
Distance:	Distance:
Time:	Time:
Zone: 1 2 3 4 5	Zone: 1 2 3 4 5
Average speed:	Average speed:
Inclination:	Inclination:
Notes:	Notes:

WEEKLY SUMMARY		
Weight	Distance	Time
Average speed	RPE: 1 – 10	
Notes:		

Week Beginning

/ /

MONDAY			
Energy	Sleep (hrs)	Sleep quality	Stress
Mood	Weather	Soreness	Weight
Injury/illness			

Ride 1	Ride 2
Resting heart rate:	Resting heart rate:
Route:	Route:
Distance:	Distance:
Time:	Time:
Zone: 1 2 3 4 5	Zone: 1 2 3 4 5
Average speed:	Average speed:
Max speed:	Max speed:
Inclination:	Inclination:
Food and water intake:	Food and water intake:
Ride report:	Ride report:
RPE: 1 – 10	RPE: 1 – 10

TUESDAY			
Energy	Sleep (hrs)	Sleep quality	Stress
Mood	Weather	Soreness	Weight
Injury/illness			

Ride 1	Ride 2
Resting heart rate:	Resting heart rate:
Route:	Route:
Distance:	Distance:
Time:	Time:
Zone: 1 2 3 4 5	Zone: 1 2 3 4 5
Average speed:	Average speed:
Max speed:	Max speed:
Inclination:	Inclination:
Food and water intake:	Food and water intake:
Ride report:	Ride report:
RPE: 1 – 10	RPE: 1 – 10

Weekly Goals

WEDNESDAY			
Energy	Sleep (hrs)	Sleep quality	Stress
Mood	Weather	Soreness	Weight
Injury/illness			

Ride 1	Ride 2
Resting heart rate:	Resting heart rate:
Route:	Route:
Distance:	Distance:
Time:	Time:
Zone: 1 2 3 4 5	Zone: 1 2 3 4 5
Average speed:	Average speed:
Max speed:	Max speed:
Inclination:	Inclination:
Food and water intake:	Food and water intake:
Ride report:	Ride report:
RPE: 1 – 10	RPE: 1 – 10

THURSDAY			
Energy	Sleep (hrs)	Sleep quality	Stress
Mood	Weather	Soreness	Weight
Injury/illness			

Ride 1	Ride 2
Resting heart rate:	Resting heart rate:
Route:	Route:
Distance:	Distance:
Time:	Time:
Zone: 1 2 3 4 5	Zone: 1 2 3 4 5
Average speed:	Average speed:
Max speed:	Max speed:
Inclination:	Inclination:
Food and water intake:	Food and water intake:
Ride report:	Ride report:
RPE: 1 – 10	RPE: 1 – 10

Week Beginning  / / Continued

FRIDAY			
Energy	Sleep (hrs)	Sleep quality	Stress
Mood	Weather	Soreness	Weight
Injury/illness			

Ride 1	Ride 2
Resting heart rate:	Resting heart rate:
Route:	Route:
Distance:	Distance:
Time:	Time:
Zone: 1 2 3 4 5	Zone: 1 2 3 4 5
Average speed:	Average speed:
Max speed:	Max speed:
Inclination:	Inclination:
Food and water intake:	Food and water intake:
Ride report:	Ride report:
RPE: 1 – 10	RPE: 1 – 10

SATURDAY			
Energy	Sleep (hrs)	Sleep quality	Stress
Mood	Weather	Soreness	Weight
Injury/illness			

Ride 1	Ride 2
Resting heart rate:	Resting heart rate:
Route:	Route:
Distance:	Distance:
Time:	Time:
Zone: 1 2 3 4 5	Zone: 1 2 3 4 5
Average speed:	Average speed:
Max speed:	Max speed:
Inclination:	Inclination:
Food and water intake:	Food and water intake:
Ride report:	Ride report:
RPE: 1 – 10	RPE: 1 – 10

SUNDAY					
Energy		Sleep (hrs)		Sleep quality	Stress
Mood		Weather		Soreness	Weight
Injury/illness					

Ride 1	Ride 2
Resting heart rate:	Resting heart rate:
Route:	Route:
Distance:	Distance:
Time:	Time:
Zone: 1 2 3 4 5	Zone: 1 2 3 4 5
Average speed:	Average speed:
Max speed:	Max speed:
Inclination:	Inclination:
Food and water intake:	Food and water intake:
Ride report:	Ride report:
RPE: 1 – 10	RPE: 1 – 10

WEEKLY COMPETITION	
Race 1	Race 2
Time Goal:	Time Goal:
Resting heart rate:	Resting heart rate:
Weather:	Weather:
Route:	Route:
Distance:	Distance:
Time:	Time:
Zone: 1 2 3 4 5	Zone: 1 2 3 4 5
Average speed:	Average speed:
Inclination:	Inclination:
Notes:	Notes:

WEEKLY SUMMARY			
Weight	Distance		Time
Average speed		RPE: 1 – 10	
Notes:			

Week Beginning

 / /

MONDAY			
Energy	Sleep (hrs)	Sleep quality	Stress
Mood	Weather	Soreness	Weight
Injury/illness			

Ride 1	Ride 2
Resting heart rate:	Resting heart rate:
Route:	Route:
Distance:	Distance:
Time:	Time:
Zone: 1 2 3 4 5	Zone: 1 2 3 4 5
Average speed:	Average speed:
Max speed:	Max speed:
Inclination:	Inclination:
Food and water intake:	Food and water intake:
Ride report:	Ride report:
RPE: 1 – 10	RPE: 1 – 10

TUESDAY			
Energy	Sleep (hrs)	Sleep quality	Stress
Mood	Weather	Soreness	Weight
Injury/illness			

Ride 1	Ride 2
Resting heart rate:	Resting heart rate:
Route:	Route:
Distance:	Distance:
Time:	Time:
Zone: 1 2 3 4 5	Zone: 1 2 3 4 5
Average speed:	Average speed:
Max speed:	Max speed:
Inclination:	Inclination:
Food and water intake:	Food and water intake:
Ride report:	Ride report:
RPE: 1 – 10	RPE: 1 – 10

Weekly Goals

WEDNESDAY			
Energy	Sleep (hrs)	Sleep quality	Stress
Mood	Weather	Soreness	Weight
Injury/illness			

Ride 1	Ride 2
Resting heart rate:	Resting heart rate:
Route:	Route:
Distance:	Distance:
Time:	Time:
Zone: 1 2 3 4 5	Zone: 1 2 3 4 5
Average speed:	Average speed:
Max speed:	Max speed:
Inclination:	Inclination:
Food and water intake:	Food and water intake:
Ride report:	Ride report:
RPE: 1 – 10	RPE: 1 – 10

THURSDAY			
Energy	Sleep (hrs)	Sleep quality	Stress
Mood	Weather	Soreness	Weight
Injury/illness			

Ride 1	Ride 2
Resting heart rate:	Resting heart rate:
Route:	Route:
Distance:	Distance:
Time:	Time:
Zone: 1 2 3 4 5	Zone: 1 2 3 4 5
Average speed:	Average speed:
Max speed:	Max speed:
Inclination:	Inclination:
Food and water intake:	Food and water intake:
Ride report:	Ride report:
RPE: 1 – 10	RPE: 1 – 10

FRIDAY			
Energy	Sleep (hrs)	Sleep quality	Stress
Mood	Weather	Soreness	Weight
Injury/illness			

Ride 1	Ride 2
Resting heart rate:	Resting heart rate:
Route:	Route:
Distance:	Distance:
Time:	Time:
Zone: 1 2 3 4 5	Zone: 1 2 3 4 5
Average speed:	Average speed:
Max speed:	Max speed:
Inclination:	Inclination:
Food and water intake:	Food and water intake:
Ride report:	Ride report:
RPE: 1 – 10	RPE: 1 – 10

SATURDAY			
Energy	Sleep (hrs)	Sleep quality	Stress
Mood	Weather	Soreness	Weight
Injury/illness			

Ride 1	Ride 2
Resting heart rate:	Resting heart rate:
Route:	Route:
Distance:	Distance:
Time:	Time:
Zone: 1 2 3 4 5	Zone: 1 2 3 4 5
Average speed:	Average speed:
Max speed:	Max speed:
Inclination:	Inclination:
Food and water intake:	Food and water intake:
Ride report:	Ride report:
RPE: 1 – 10	RPE: 1 – 10

SUNDAY			
Energy	Sleep (hrs)	Sleep quality	Stress
Mood	Weather	Soreness	Weight
Injury/illness			

Ride 1	Ride 2
Resting heart rate:	Resting heart rate:
Route:	Route:
Distance:	Distance:
Time:	Time:
Zone: 1 2 3 4 5	Zone: 1 2 3 4 5
Average speed:	Average speed:
Max speed:	Max speed:
Inclination:	Inclination:
Food and water intake:	Food and water intake:
Ride report:	Ride report:
RPE: 1 – 10	RPE: 1 – 10

WEEKLY COMPETITION	
Race 1	Race 2
Time Goal:	Time Goal:
Resting heart rate:	Resting heart rate:
Weather:	Weather:
Route:	Route:
Distance:	Distance:
Time:	Time:
Zone: 1 2 3 4 5	Zone: 1 2 3 4 5
Average speed:	Average speed:
Inclination:	Inclination:
Notes:	Notes:

WEEKLY SUMMARY		
Weight	Distance	Time
Average speed	RPE: 1 – 10	
Notes:		

Week Beginning

 / /

MONDAY			
Energy	Sleep (hrs)	Sleep quality	Stress
Mood	Weather	Soreness	Weight
Injury/illness			

Ride 1	Ride 2
Resting heart rate:	Resting heart rate:
Route:	Route:
Distance:	Distance:
Time:	Time:
Zone: 1 2 3 4 5	Zone: 1 2 3 4 5
Average speed:	Average speed:
Max speed:	Max speed:
Inclination:	Inclination:
Food and water intake:	Food and water intake:
Ride report:	Ride report:
RPE: 1 – 10	RPE: 1 – 10

TUESDAY			
Energy	Sleep (hrs)	Sleep quality	Stress
Mood	Weather	Soreness	Weight
Injury/illness			

Ride 1	Ride 2
Resting heart rate:	Resting heart rate:
Route:	Route:
Distance:	Distance:
Time:	Time:
Zone: 1 2 3 4 5	Zone: 1 2 3 4 5
Average speed:	Average speed:
Max speed:	Max speed:
Inclination:	Inclination:
Food and water intake:	Food and water intake:
Ride report:	Ride report:
RPE: 1 – 10	RPE: 1 – 10

Weekly Goals

WEDNESDAY			
Energy	Sleep (hrs)	Sleep quality	Stress
Mood	Weather	Soreness	Weight
Injury/illness			

Ride 1	Ride 2
Resting heart rate:	Resting heart rate:
Route:	Route:
Distance:	Distance:
Time:	Time:
Zone: 1 2 3 4 5	Zone: 1 2 3 4 5
Average speed:	Average speed:
Max speed:	Max speed:
Inclination:	Inclination:
Food and water intake:	Food and water intake:
Ride report:	Ride report:
RPE: 1 – 10	RPE: 1 – 10

THURSDAY			
Energy	Sleep (hrs)	Sleep quality	Stress
Mood	Weather	Soreness	Weight
Injury/illness			

Ride 1	Ride 2
Resting heart rate:	Resting heart rate:
Route:	Route:
Distance:	Distance:
Time:	Time:
Zone: 1 2 3 4 5	Zone: 1 2 3 4 5
Average speed:	Average speed:
Max speed:	Max speed:
Inclination:	Inclination:
Food and water intake:	Food and water intake:
Ride report:	Ride report:
RPE: 1 – 10	RPE: 1 – 10

Week Beginning / / Continued

FRIDAY			
Energy	Sleep (hrs)	Sleep quality	Stress
Mood	Weather	Soreness	Weight
Injury/illness			

Ride 1	Ride 2
Resting heart rate:	Resting heart rate:
Route:	Route:
Distance:	Distance:
Time:	Time:
Zone: 1 2 3 4 5	Zone: 1 2 3 4 5
Average speed:	Average speed:
Max speed:	Max speed:
Inclination:	Inclination:
Food and water intake:	Food and water intake:
Ride report:	Ride report:
RPE: 1 – 10	RPE: 1 – 10

SATURDAY			
Energy	Sleep (hrs)	Sleep quality	Stress
Mood	Weather	Soreness	Weight
Injury/illness			

Ride 1	Ride 2
Resting heart rate:	Resting heart rate:
Route:	Route:
Distance:	Distance:
Time:	Time:
Zone: 1 2 3 4 5	Zone: 1 2 3 4 5
Average speed:	Average speed:
Max speed:	Max speed:
Inclination:	Inclination:
Food and water intake:	Food and water intake:
Ride report:	Ride report:
RPE: 1 – 10	RPE: 1 – 10

SUNDAY			
Energy	Sleep (hrs)	Sleep quality	Stress
Mood	Weather	Soreness	Weight
Injury/illness			

Ride 1	Ride 2
Resting heart rate:	Resting heart rate:
Route:	Route:
Distance:	Distance:
Time:	Time:
Zone:　1　　2　　3　　4　　5	Zone:　1　　2　　3　　4　　5
Average speed:	Average speed:
Max speed:	Max speed:
Inclination:	Inclination:
Food and water intake:	Food and water intake:
Ride report:	Ride report:
RPE: 1 – 10	RPE: 1 – 10

WEEKLY COMPETITION	
Race 1	Race 2
Time Goal:	Time Goal:
Resting heart rate:	Resting heart rate:
Weather:	Weather:
Route:	Route:
Distance:	Distance:
Time:	Time:
Zone:　1　　2　　3　　4　　5	Zone:　1　　2　　3　　4　　5
Average speed:	Average speed:
Inclination:	Inclination:
Notes:	Notes:

WEEKLY SUMMARY		
Weight	Distance	Time
Average speed	RPE: 1 – 10	
Notes:		

Week Beginning

   /   /

MONDAY			
Energy	Sleep (hrs)	Sleep quality	Stress
Mood	Weather	Soreness	Weight
Injury/illness			

Ride 1	Ride 2
Resting heart rate:	Resting heart rate:
Route:	Route:
Distance:	Distance:
Time:	Time:
Zone:　1　　2　　3　　4　　5	Zone:　1　　2　　3　　4　　5
Average speed:	Average speed:
Max speed:	Max speed:
Inclination:	Inclination:
Food and water intake:	Food and water intake:
Ride report:	Ride report:
RPE: 1 – 10	RPE: 1 – 10

TUESDAY			
Energy	Sleep (hrs)	Sleep quality	Stress
Mood	Weather	Soreness	Weight
Injury/illness			

Ride 1	Ride 2
Resting heart rate:	Resting heart rate:
Route:	Route:
Distance:	Distance:
Time:	Time:
Zone:　1　　2　　3　　4　　5	Zone:　1　　2　　3　　4　　5
Average speed:	Average speed:
Max speed:	Max speed:
Inclination:	Inclination:
Food and water intake:	Food and water intake:
Ride report:	Ride report:
RPE: 1 – 10	RPE: 1 – 10

Weekly Goals

WEDNESDAY			
Energy	Sleep (hrs)	Sleep quality	Stress
Mood	Weather	Soreness	Weight
Injury/illness			

Ride 1	Ride 2
Resting heart rate:	Resting heart rate:
Route:	Route:
Distance:	Distance:
Time:	Time:
Zone: 1 2 3 4 5	Zone: 1 2 3 4 5
Average speed:	Average speed:
Max speed:	Max speed:
Inclination:	Inclination:
Food and water intake:	Food and water intake:
Ride report:	Ride report:
RPE: 1 – 10	RPE: 1 – 10

THURSDAY			
Energy	Sleep (hrs)	Sleep quality	Stress
Mood	Weather	Soreness	Weight
Injury/illness			

Ride 1	Ride 2
Resting heart rate:	Resting heart rate:
Route:	Route:
Distance:	Distance:
Time:	Time:
Zone: 1 2 3 4 5	Zone: 1 2 3 4 5
Average speed:	Average speed:
Max speed:	Max speed:
Inclination:	Inclination:
Food and water intake:	Food and water intake:
Ride report:	Ride report:
RPE: 1 – 10	RPE: 1 – 10

FRIDAY			
Energy	Sleep (hrs)	Sleep quality	Stress
Mood	Weather	Soreness	Weight
Injury/illness			

Ride 1	Ride 2
Resting heart rate:	Resting heart rate:
Route:	Route:
Distance:	Distance:
Time:	Time:
Zone: 1 2 3 4 5	Zone: 1 2 3 4 5
Average speed:	Average speed:
Max speed:	Max speed:
Inclination:	Inclination:
Food and water intake:	Food and water intake:
Ride report:	Ride report:
RPE: 1 – 10	RPE: 1 – 10

SATURDAY			
Energy	Sleep (hrs)	Sleep quality	Stress
Mood	Weather	Soreness	Weight
Injury/illness			

Ride 1	Ride 2
Resting heart rate:	Resting heart rate:
Route:	Route:
Distance:	Distance:
Time:	Time:
Zone: 1 2 3 4 5	Zone: 1 2 3 4 5
Average speed:	Average speed:
Max speed:	Max speed:
Inclination:	Inclination:
Food and water intake:	Food and water intake:
Ride report:	Ride report:
RPE: 1 – 10	RPE: 1 – 10

SUNDAY			
Energy	Sleep (hrs)	Sleep quality	Stress
Mood	Weather	Soreness	Weight
Injury/illness			

Ride 1	Ride 2
Resting heart rate:	Resting heart rate:
Route:	Route:
Distance:	Distance:
Time:	Time:
Zone: 1 2 3 4 5	Zone: 1 2 3 4 5
Average speed:	Average speed:
Max speed:	Max speed:
Inclination:	Inclination:
Food and water intake:	Food and water intake:
Ride report:	Ride report:
RPE: 1 – 10	RPE: 1 – 10

WEEKLY COMPETITION	
Race 1	Race 2
Time Goal:	Time Goal:
Resting heart rate:	Resting heart rate:
Weather:	Weather:
Route:	Route:
Distance:	Distance:
Time:	Time:
Zone: 1 2 3 4 5	Zone: 1 2 3 4 5
Average speed:	Average speed:
Inclination:	Inclination:
Notes:	Notes:

WEEKLY SUMMARY		
Weight	Distance	Time
Average speed	RPE: 1 – 10	
Notes:		

Week Beginning

 / /

MONDAY			
Energy	Sleep (hrs)	Sleep quality	Stress
Mood	Weather	Soreness	Weight
Injury/illness			

Ride 1	Ride 2
Resting heart rate:	Resting heart rate:
Route:	Route:
Distance:	Distance:
Time:	Time:
Zone: 1 2 3 4 5	Zone: 1 2 3 4 5
Average speed:	Average speed:
Max speed:	Max speed:
Inclination:	Inclination:
Food and water intake:	Food and water intake:
Ride report:	Ride report:
RPE: 1 – 10	RPE: 1 – 10

TUESDAY			
Energy	Sleep (hrs)	Sleep quality	Stress
Mood	Weather	Soreness	Weight
Injury/illness			

Ride 1	Ride 2
Resting heart rate:	Resting heart rate:
Route:	Route:
Distance:	Distance:
Time:	Time:
Zone: 1 2 3 4 5	Zone: 1 2 3 4 5
Average speed:	Average speed:
Max speed:	Max speed:
Inclination:	Inclination:
Food and water intake:	Food and water intake:
Ride report:	Ride report:
RPE: 1 – 10	RPE: 1 – 10

Weekly Goals

WEDNESDAY			
Energy	Sleep (hrs)	Sleep quality	Stress
Mood	Weather	Soreness	Weight
Injury/illness			

Ride 1	Ride 2
Resting heart rate:	Resting heart rate:
Route:	Route:
Distance:	Distance:
Time:	Time:
Zone: 1 2 3 4 5	Zone: 1 2 3 4 5
Average speed:	Average speed:
Max speed:	Max speed:
Inclination:	Inclination:
Food and water intake:	Food and water intake:
Ride report:	Ride report:
RPE: 1 – 10	RPE: 1 – 10

THURSDAY			
Energy	Sleep (hrs)	Sleep quality	Stress
Mood	Weather	Soreness	Weight
Injury/illness			

Ride 1	Ride 2
Resting heart rate:	Resting heart rate:
Route:	Route:
Distance:	Distance:
Time:	Time:
Zone: 1 2 3 4 5	Zone: 1 2 3 4 5
Average speed:	Average speed:
Max speed:	Max speed:
Inclination:	Inclination:
Food and water intake:	Food and water intake:
Ride report:	Ride report:
RPE: 1 – 10	RPE: 1 – 10

FRIDAY			
Energy	Sleep (hrs)	Sleep quality	Stress
Mood	Weather	Soreness	Weight
Injury/illness			

Ride 1	Ride 2
Resting heart rate:	Resting heart rate:
Route:	Route:
Distance:	Distance:
Time:	Time:
Zone: 1 2 3 4 5	Zone: 1 2 3 4 5
Average speed:	Average speed:
Max speed:	Max speed:
Inclination:	Inclination:
Food and water intake:	Food and water intake:
Ride report:	Ride report:
RPE: 1 – 10	RPE: 1 – 10

SATURDAY			
Energy	Sleep (hrs)	Sleep quality	Stress
Mood	Weather	Soreness	Weight
Injury/illness			

Ride 1	Ride 2
Resting heart rate:	Resting heart rate:
Route:	Route:
Distance:	Distance:
Time:	Time:
Zone: 1 2 3 4 5	Zone: 1 2 3 4 5
Average speed:	Average speed:
Max speed:	Max speed:
Inclination:	Inclination:
Food and water intake:	Food and water intake:
Ride report:	Ride report:
RPE: 1 – 10	RPE: 1 – 10

SUNDAY			
Energy	Sleep (hrs)	Sleep quality	Stress
Mood	Weather	Soreness	Weight
Injury/illness			

Ride 1	Ride 2
Resting heart rate:	Resting heart rate:
Route:	Route:
Distance:	Distance:
Time:	Time:
Zone: 1 2 3 4 5	Zone: 1 2 3 4 5
Average speed:	Average speed:
Max speed:	Max speed:
Inclination:	Inclination:
Food and water intake:	Food and water intake:
Ride report:	Ride report:
RPE: 1 – 10	RPE: 1 – 10

WEEKLY COMPETITION	
Race 1	Race 2
Time Goal:	Time Goal:
Resting heart rate:	Resting heart rate:
Weather:	Weather:
Route:	Route:
Distance:	Distance:
Time:	Time:
Zone: 1 2 3 4 5	Zone: 1 2 3 4 5
Average speed:	Average speed:
Inclination:	Inclination:
Notes:	Notes:

WEEKLY SUMMARY		
Weight	Distance	Time
Average speed	RPE: 1 – 10	
Notes:		

Week Beginning

/   /

MONDAY			
Energy	Sleep (hrs)	Sleep quality	Stress
Mood	Weather	Soreness	Weight
Injury/illness			

Ride 1	Ride 2
Resting heart rate:	Resting heart rate:
Route:	Route:
Distance:	Distance:
Time:	Time:
Zone: 1 2 3 4 5	Zone: 1 2 3 4 5
Average speed:	Average speed:
Max speed:	Max speed:
Inclination:	Inclination:
Food and water intake:	Food and water intake:
Ride report:	Ride report:
RPE: 1 – 10	RPE: 1 – 10

TUESDAY			
Energy	Sleep (hrs)	Sleep quality	Stress
Mood	Weather	Soreness	Weight
Injury/illness			

Ride 1	Ride 2
Resting heart rate:	Resting heart rate:
Route:	Route:
Distance:	Distance:
Time:	Time:
Zone: 1 2 3 4 5	Zone: 1 2 3 4 5
Average speed:	Average speed:
Max speed:	Max speed:
Inclination:	Inclination:
Food and water intake:	Food and water intake:
Ride report:	Ride report:
RPE: 1 – 10	RPE: 1 – 10

Weekly Goals

WEDNESDAY			
Energy	Sleep (hrs)	Sleep quality	Stress
Mood	Weather	Soreness	Weight
Injury/illness			

Ride 1	Ride 2
Resting heart rate:	Resting heart rate:
Route:	Route:
Distance:	Distance:
Time:	Time:
Zone: 1 2 3 4 5	Zone: 1 2 3 4 5
Average speed:	Average speed:
Max speed:	Max speed:
Inclination:	Inclination:
Food and water intake:	Food and water intake:
Ride report:	Ride report:
RPE: 1 – 10	RPE: 1 – 10

THURSDAY			
Energy	Sleep (hrs)	Sleep quality	Stress
Mood	Weather	Soreness	Weight
Injury/illness			

Ride 1	Ride 2
Resting heart rate:	Resting heart rate:
Route:	Route:
Distance:	Distance:
Time:	Time:
Zone: 1 2 3 4 5	Zone: 1 2 3 4 5
Average speed:	Average speed:
Max speed:	Max speed:
Inclination:	Inclination:
Food and water intake:	Food and water intake:
Ride report:	Ride report:
RPE: 1 – 10	RPE: 1 – 10

FRIDAY			
Energy	Sleep (hrs)	Sleep quality	Stress
Mood	Weather	Soreness	Weight
Injury/illness			

Ride 1	Ride 2
Resting heart rate:	Resting heart rate:
Route:	Route:
Distance:	Distance:
Time:	Time:
Zone: 1 2 3 4 5	Zone: 1 2 3 4 5
Average speed:	Average speed:
Max speed:	Max speed:
Inclination:	Inclination:
Food and water intake:	Food and water intake:
Ride report:	Ride report:
RPE: 1 – 10	RPE: 1 – 10

SATURDAY			
Energy	Sleep (hrs)	Sleep quality	Stress
Mood	Weather	Soreness	Weight
Injury/illness			

Ride 1	Ride 2
Resting heart rate:	Resting heart rate:
Route:	Route:
Distance:	Distance:
Time:	Time:
Zone: 1 2 3 4 5	Zone: 1 2 3 4 5
Average speed:	Average speed:
Max speed:	Max speed:
Inclination:	Inclination:
Food and water intake:	Food and water intake:
Ride report:	Ride report:
RPE: 1 – 10	RPE: 1 – 10

SUNDAY

Energy		Sleep (hrs)		Sleep quality		Stress	
Mood		Weather		Soreness		Weight	
Injury/illness							

Ride 1	Ride 2
Resting heart rate:	Resting heart rate:
Route:	Route:
Distance:	Distance:
Time:	Time:
Zone: 1 2 3 4 5	Zone: 1 2 3 4 5
Average speed:	Average speed:
Max speed:	Max speed:
Inclination:	Inclination:
Food and water intake:	Food and water intake:
Ride report:	Ride report:
RPE: 1 – 10	RPE: 1 – 10

WEEKLY COMPETITION

Race 1	Race 2
Time Goal:	Time Goal:
Resting heart rate:	Resting heart rate:
Weather:	Weather:
Route:	Route:
Distance:	Distance:
Time:	Time:
Zone: 1 2 3 4 5	Zone: 1 2 3 4 5
Average speed:	Average speed:
Inclination:	Inclination:
Notes:	Notes:

WEEKLY SUMMARY

Weight		Distance		Time	
Average speed		RPE: 1 – 10			
Notes:					

Week Beginning

/ /

MONDAY							
Energy		Sleep (hrs)		Sleep quality		Stress	
Mood		Weather		Soreness		Weight	
Injury/illness							

Ride 1	Ride 2
Resting heart rate:	Resting heart rate:
Route:	Route:
Distance:	Distance:
Time:	Time:
Zone: 1 2 3 4 5	Zone: 1 2 3 4 5
Average speed:	Average speed:
Max speed:	Max speed:
Inclination:	Inclination:
Food and water intake:	Food and water intake:
Ride report:	Ride report:
RPE: 1 – 10	RPE: 1 – 10

TUESDAY							
Energy		Sleep (hrs)		Sleep quality		Stress	
Mood		Weather		Soreness		Weight	
Injury/illness							

Ride 1	Ride 2
Resting heart rate:	Resting heart rate:
Route:	Route:
Distance:	Distance:
Time:	Time:
Zone: 1 2 3 4 5	Zone: 1 2 3 4 5
Average speed:	Average speed:
Max speed:	Max speed:
Inclination:	Inclination:
Food and water intake:	Food and water intake:
Ride report:	Ride report:
RPE: 1 – 10	RPE: 1 – 10

Weekly Goals

WEDNESDAY			
Energy	Sleep (hrs)	Sleep quality	Stress
Mood	Weather	Soreness	Weight
Injury/illness			

Ride 1	Ride 2
Resting heart rate:	Resting heart rate:
Route:	Route:
Distance:	Distance:
Time:	Time:
Zone: 1 2 3 4 5	Zone: 1 2 3 4 5
Average speed:	Average speed:
Max speed:	Max speed:
Inclination:	Inclination:
Food and water intake:	Food and water intake:
Ride report:	Ride report:
RPE: 1 – 10	RPE: 1 – 10

THURSDAY			
Energy	Sleep (hrs)	Sleep quality	Stress
Mood	Weather	Soreness	Weight
Injury/illness			

Ride 1	Ride 2
Resting heart rate:	Resting heart rate:
Route:	Route:
Distance:	Distance:
Time:	Time:
Zone: 1 2 3 4 5	Zone: 1 2 3 4 5
Average speed:	Average speed:
Max speed:	Max speed:
Inclination:	Inclination:
Food and water intake:	Food and water intake:
Ride report:	Ride report:
RPE: 1 – 10	RPE: 1 – 10

Week Beginning  / / Continued

FRIDAY			
Energy	Sleep (hrs)	Sleep quality	Stress
Mood	Weather	Soreness	Weight
Injury/illness			

Ride 1		Ride 2	
Resting heart rate:		Resting heart rate:	
Route:		Route:	
Distance:		Distance:	
Time:		Time:	
Zone: 1 2 3 4 5		Zone: 1 2 3 4 5	
Average speed:		Average speed:	
Max speed:		Max speed:	
Inclination:		Inclination:	
Food and water intake:		Food and water intake:	
Ride report:		Ride report:	
RPE: 1 – 10		RPE: 1 – 10	

SATURDAY			
Energy	Sleep (hrs)	Sleep quality	Stress
Mood	Weather	Soreness	Weight
Injury/illness			

Ride 1		Ride 2	
Resting heart rate:		Resting heart rate:	
Route:		Route:	
Distance:		Distance:	
Time:		Time:	
Zone: 1 2 3 4 5		Zone: 1 2 3 4 5	
Average speed:		Average speed:	
Max speed:		Max speed:	
Inclination:		Inclination:	
Food and water intake:		Food and water intake:	
Ride report:		Ride report:	
RPE: 1 – 10		RPE: 1 – 10	

SUNDAY			
Energy	Sleep (hrs)	Sleep quality	Stress
Mood	Weather	Soreness	Weight
Injury/illness			

Ride 1	Ride 2
Resting heart rate:	Resting heart rate:
Route:	Route:
Distance:	Distance:
Time:	Time:
Zone: 1 2 3 4 5	Zone: 1 2 3 4 5
Average speed:	Average speed:
Max speed:	Max speed:
Inclination:	Inclination:
Food and water intake:	Food and water intake:
Ride report:	Ride report:
RPE: 1 – 10	RPE: 1 – 10

WEEKLY COMPETITION	
Race 1	Race 2
Time Goal:	Time Goal:
Resting heart rate:	Resting heart rate:
Weather:	Weather:
Route:	Route:
Distance:	Distance:
Time:	Time:
Zone: 1 2 3 4 5	Zone: 1 2 3 4 5
Average speed:	Average speed:
Inclination:	Inclination:
Notes:	Notes:

WEEKLY SUMMARY		
Weight	Distance	Time
Average speed	RPE: 1 – 10	
Notes:		

Week Beginning

/ /

MONDAY			
Energy	Sleep (hrs)	Sleep quality	Stress
Mood	Weather	Soreness	Weight
Injury/illness			

Ride 1	Ride 2
Resting heart rate:	Resting heart rate:
Route:	Route:
Distance:	Distance:
Time:	Time:
Zone: 1 2 3 4 5	Zone: 1 2 3 4 5
Average speed:	Average speed:
Max speed:	Max speed:
Inclination:	Inclination:
Food and water intake:	Food and water intake:
Ride report:	Ride report:
RPE: 1 – 10	RPE: 1 – 10

TUESDAY			
Energy	Sleep (hrs)	Sleep quality	Stress
Mood	Weather	Soreness	Weight
Injury/illness			

Ride 1	Ride 2
Resting heart rate:	Resting heart rate:
Route:	Route:
Distance:	Distance:
Time:	Time:
Zone: 1 2 3 4 5	Zone: 1 2 3 4 5
Average speed:	Average speed:
Max speed:	Max speed:
Inclination:	Inclination:
Food and water intake:	Food and water intake:
Ride report:	Ride report:
RPE: 1 – 10	RPE: 1 – 10

Weekly Goals

WEDNESDAY			
Energy	Sleep (hrs)	Sleep quality	Stress
Mood	Weather	Soreness	Weight
Injury/illness			

Ride 1		Ride 2	
Resting heart rate:		Resting heart rate:	
Route:		Route:	
Distance:		Distance:	
Time:		Time:	
Zone: 1 2 3 4 5		Zone: 1 2 3 4 5	
Average speed:		Average speed:	
Max speed:		Max speed:	
Inclination:		Inclination:	
Food and water intake:		Food and water intake:	
Ride report:		Ride report:	
RPE: 1 – 10		RPE: 1 – 10	

THURSDAY			
Energy	Sleep (hrs)	Sleep quality	Stress
Mood	Weather	Soreness	Weight
Injury/illness			

Ride 1		Ride 2	
Resting heart rate:		Resting heart rate:	
Route:		Route:	
Distance:		Distance:	
Time:		Time:	
Zone: 1 2 3 4 5		Zone: 1 2 3 4 5	
Average speed:		Average speed:	
Max speed:		Max speed:	
Inclination:		Inclination:	
Food and water intake:		Food and water intake:	
Ride report:		Ride report:	
RPE: 1 – 10		RPE: 1 – 10	

Week Beginning  / / Continued

FRIDAY			
Energy	Sleep (hrs)	Sleep quality	Stress
Mood	Weather	Soreness	Weight
Injury/illness			

Ride 1	Ride 2
Resting heart rate:	Resting heart rate:
Route:	Route:
Distance:	Distance:
Time:	Time:
Zone: 1 2 3 4 5	Zone: 1 2 3 4 5
Average speed:	Average speed:
Max speed:	Max speed:
Inclination:	Inclination:
Food and water intake:	Food and water intake:
Ride report:	Ride report:
RPE: 1 – 10	RPE: 1 – 10

SATURDAY			
Energy	Sleep (hrs)	Sleep quality	Stress
Mood	Weather	Soreness	Weight
Injury/illness			

Ride 1	Ride 2
Resting heart rate:	Resting heart rate:
Route:	Route:
Distance:	Distance:
Time:	Time:
Zone: 1 2 3 4 5	Zone: 1 2 3 4 5
Average speed:	Average speed:
Max speed:	Max speed:
Inclination:	Inclination:
Food and water intake:	Food and water intake:
Ride report:	Ride report:
RPE: 1 – 10	RPE: 1 – 10

SUNDAY

Energy		Sleep (hrs)		Sleep quality		Stress	
Mood		Weather		Soreness		Weight	
Injury/illness							

Ride 1	Ride 2
Resting heart rate:	Resting heart rate:
Route:	Route:
Distance:	Distance:
Time:	Time:
Zone: 1 2 3 4 5	Zone: 1 2 3 4 5
Average speed:	Average speed:
Max speed:	Max speed:
Inclination:	Inclination:
Food and water intake:	Food and water intake:
Ride report:	Ride report:
RPE: 1 – 10	RPE: 1 – 10

WEEKLY COMPETITION

Race 1	Race 2
Time Goal:	Time Goal:
Resting heart rate:	Resting heart rate:
Weather:	Weather:
Route:	Route:
Distance:	Distance:
Time:	Time:
Zone: 1 2 3 4 5	Zone: 1 2 3 4 5
Average speed:	Average speed:
Inclination:	Inclination:
Notes:	Notes:

WEEKLY SUMMARY

Weight		Distance		Time	
Average speed		RPE: 1 – 10			
Notes:					

Week Beginning    /   /

MONDAY			
Energy	Sleep (hrs)	Sleep quality	Stress
Mood	Weather	Soreness	Weight
Injury/illness			

Ride 1	Ride 2
Resting heart rate:	Resting heart rate:
Route:	Route:
Distance:	Distance:
Time:	Time:
Zone: 1 2 3 4 5	Zone: 1 2 3 4 5
Average speed:	Average speed:
Max speed:	Max speed:
Inclination:	Inclination:
Food and water intake:	Food and water intake:
Ride report:	Ride report:
RPE: 1 – 10	RPE: 1 – 10

TUESDAY			
Energy	Sleep (hrs)	Sleep quality	Stress
Mood	Weather	Soreness	Weight
Injury/illness			

Ride 1	Ride 2
Resting heart rate:	Resting heart rate:
Route:	Route:
Distance:	Distance:
Time:	Time:
Zone: 1 2 3 4 5	Zone: 1 2 3 4 5
Average speed:	Average speed:
Max speed:	Max speed:
Inclination:	Inclination:
Food and water intake:	Food and water intake:
Ride report:	Ride report:
RPE: 1 – 10	RPE: 1 – 10

Weekly Goals

WEDNESDAY			
Energy	Sleep (hrs)	Sleep quality	Stress
Mood	Weather	Soreness	Weight
Injury/illness			

Ride 1	Ride 2
Resting heart rate:	Resting heart rate:
Route:	Route:
Distance:	Distance:
Time:	Time:
Zone: 1 2 3 4 5	Zone: 1 2 3 4 5
Average speed:	Average speed:
Max speed:	Max speed:
Inclination:	Inclination:
Food and water intake:	Food and water intake:
Ride report:	Ride report:
RPE: 1 – 10	RPE: 1 – 10

THURSDAY			
Energy	Sleep (hrs)	Sleep quality	Stress
Mood	Weather	Soreness	Weight
Injury/illness			

Ride 1	Ride 2
Resting heart rate:	Resting heart rate:
Route:	Route:
Distance:	Distance:
Time:	Time:
Zone: 1 2 3 4 5	Zone: 1 2 3 4 5
Average speed:	Average speed:
Max speed:	Max speed:
Inclination:	Inclination:
Food and water intake:	Food and water intake:
Ride report:	Ride report:
RPE: 1 – 10	RPE: 1 – 10

Week Beginning / / Continued

FRIDAY			
Energy	Sleep (hrs)	Sleep quality	Stress
Mood	Weather	Soreness	Weight
Injury/illness			

Ride 1	Ride 2
Resting heart rate:	Resting heart rate:
Route:	Route:
Distance:	Distance:
Time:	Time:
Zone: 1 2 3 4 5	Zone: 1 2 3 4 5
Average speed:	Average speed:
Max speed:	Max speed:
Inclination:	Inclination:
Food and water intake:	Food and water intake:
Ride report:	Ride report:
RPE: 1 – 10	RPE: 1 – 10

SATURDAY			
Energy	Sleep (hrs)	Sleep quality	Stress
Mood	Weather	Soreness	Weight
Injury/illness			

Ride 1	Ride 2
Resting heart rate:	Resting heart rate:
Route:	Route:
Distance:	Distance:
Time:	Time:
Zone: 1 2 3 4 5	Zone: 1 2 3 4 5
Average speed:	Average speed:
Max speed:	Max speed:
Inclination:	Inclination:
Food and water intake:	Food and water intake:
Ride report:	Ride report:
RPE: 1 – 10	RPE: 1 – 10

SUNDAY			
Energy	Sleep (hrs)	Sleep quality	Stress
Mood	Weather	Soreness	Weight
Injury/illness			

Ride 1	Ride 2
Resting heart rate:	Resting heart rate:
Route:	Route:
Distance:	Distance:
Time:	Time:
Zone: 1 2 3 4 5	Zone: 1 2 3 4 5
Average speed:	Average speed:
Max speed:	Max speed:
Inclination:	Inclination:
Food and water intake:	Food and water intake:
Ride report:	Ride report:
RPE: 1 – 10	RPE: 1 – 10

WEEKLY COMPETITION	
Race 1	Race 2
Time Goal:	Time Goal:
Resting heart rate:	Resting heart rate:
Weather:	Weather:
Route:	Route:
Distance:	Distance:
Time:	Time:
Zone: 1 2 3 4 5	Zone: 1 2 3 4 5
Average speed:	Average speed:
Inclination:	Inclination:
Notes:	Notes:

WEEKLY SUMMARY		
Weight	Distance	Time
Average speed	RPE: 1 – 10	
Notes:		

Week Beginning

/   /

MONDAY			
Energy	Sleep (hrs)	Sleep quality	Stress
Mood	Weather	Soreness	Weight
Injury/illness			

Ride 1		Ride 2	
Resting heart rate:		Resting heart rate:	
Route:		Route:	
Distance:		Distance:	
Time:		Time:	
Zone: 1 2 3 4 5		Zone: 1 2 3 4 5	
Average speed:		Average speed:	
Max speed:		Max speed:	
Inclination:		Inclination:	
Food and water intake:		Food and water intake:	
Ride report:		Ride report:	
RPE: 1 – 10		RPE: 1 – 10	

TUESDAY			
Energy	Sleep (hrs)	Sleep quality	Stress
Mood	Weather	Soreness	Weight
Injury/illness			

Ride 1		Ride 2	
Resting heart rate:		Resting heart rate:	
Route:		Route:	
Distance:		Distance:	
Time:		Time:	
Zone: 1 2 3 4 5		Zone: 1 2 3 4 5	
Average speed:		Average speed:	
Max speed:		Max speed:	
Inclination:		Inclination:	
Food and water intake:		Food and water intake:	
Ride report:		Ride report:	
RPE: 1 – 10		RPE: 1 – 10	

Weekly Goals

WEDNESDAY			
Energy	Sleep (hrs)	Sleep quality	Stress
Mood	Weather	Soreness	Weight
Injury/illness			

Ride 1	Ride 2
Resting heart rate:	Resting heart rate:
Route:	Route:
Distance:	Distance:
Time:	Time:
Zone: 1 2 3 4 5	Zone: 1 2 3 4 5
Average speed:	Average speed:
Max speed:	Max speed:
Inclination:	Inclination:
Food and water intake:	Food and water intake:
Ride report:	Ride report:
RPE: 1 – 10	RPE: 1 – 10

THURSDAY			
Energy	Sleep (hrs)	Sleep quality	Stress
Mood	Weather	Soreness	Weight
Injury/illness			

Ride 1	Ride 2
Resting heart rate:	Resting heart rate:
Route:	Route:
Distance:	Distance:
Time:	Time:
Zone: 1 2 3 4 5	Zone: 1 2 3 4 5
Average speed:	Average speed:
Max speed:	Max speed:
Inclination:	Inclination:
Food and water intake:	Food and water intake:
Ride report:	Ride report:
RPE: 1 – 10	RPE: 1 – 10

Week Beginning / / Continued

FRIDAY			
Energy	Sleep (hrs)	Sleep quality	Stress
Mood	Weather	Soreness	Weight
Injury/illness			

Ride 1	Ride 2
Resting heart rate:	Resting heart rate:
Route:	Route:
Distance:	Distance:
Time:	Time:
Zone: 1 2 3 4 5	Zone: 1 2 3 4 5
Average speed:	Average speed:
Max speed:	Max speed:
Inclination:	Inclination:
Food and water intake:	Food and water intake:
Ride report:	Ride report:
RPE: 1 – 10	RPE: 1 – 10

SATURDAY			
Energy	Sleep (hrs)	Sleep quality	Stress
Mood	Weather	Soreness	Weight
Injury/illness			

Ride 1	Ride 2
Resting heart rate:	Resting heart rate:
Route:	Route:
Distance:	Distance:
Time:	Time:
Zone: 1 2 3 4 5	Zone: 1 2 3 4 5
Average speed:	Average speed:
Max speed:	Max speed:
Inclination:	Inclination:
Food and water intake:	Food and water intake:
Ride report:	Ride report:
RPE: 1 – 10	RPE: 1 – 10

SUNDAY

Energy		Sleep (hrs)		Sleep quality		Stress	
Mood		Weather		Soreness		Weight	
Injury/illness							

Ride 1	Ride 2
Resting heart rate:	Resting heart rate:
Route:	Route:
Distance:	Distance:
Time:	Time:
Zone: 1 2 3 4 5	Zone: 1 2 3 4 5
Average speed:	Average speed:
Max speed:	Max speed:
Inclination:	Inclination:
Food and water intake:	Food and water intake:
Ride report:	Ride report:
RPE: 1 – 10	RPE: 1 – 10

WEEKLY COMPETITION

Race 1	Race 2
Time Goal:	Time Goal:
Resting heart rate:	Resting heart rate:
Weather:	Weather:
Route:	Route:
Distance:	Distance:
Time:	Time:
Zone: 1 2 3 4 5	Zone: 1 2 3 4 5
Average speed:	Average speed:
Inclination:	Inclination:
Notes:	Notes:

WEEKLY SUMMARY

Weight		Distance		Time	
Average speed		RPE: 1 – 10			
Notes:					

Week Beginning

 / /

MONDAY			
Energy	Sleep (hrs)	Sleep quality	Stress
Mood	Weather	Soreness	Weight
Injury/illness			

Ride 1	Ride 2
Resting heart rate:	Resting heart rate:
Route:	Route:
Distance:	Distance:
Time:	Time:
Zone: 1 2 3 4 5	Zone: 1 2 3 4 5
Average speed:	Average speed:
Max speed:	Max speed:
Inclination:	Inclination:
Food and water intake:	Food and water intake:
Ride report:	Ride report:
RPE: 1 – 10	RPE: 1 – 10

TUESDAY			
Energy	Sleep (hrs)	Sleep quality	Stress
Mood	Weather	Soreness	Weight
Injury/illness			

Ride 1	Ride 2
Resting heart rate:	Resting heart rate:
Route:	Route:
Distance:	Distance:
Time:	Time:
Zone: 1 2 3 4 5	Zone: 1 2 3 4 5
Average speed:	Average speed:
Max speed:	Max speed:
Inclination:	Inclination:
Food and water intake:	Food and water intake:
Ride report:	Ride report:
RPE: 1 – 10	RPE: 1 – 10

Weekly Goals

WEDNESDAY			
Energy	Sleep (hrs)	Sleep quality	Stress
Mood	Weather	Soreness	Weight
Injury/illness			

Ride 1	Ride 2
Resting heart rate:	Resting heart rate:
Route:	Route:
Distance:	Distance:
Time:	Time:
Zone: 1 2 3 4 5	Zone: 1 2 3 4 5
Average speed:	Average speed:
Max speed:	Max speed:
Inclination:	Inclination:
Food and water intake:	Food and water intake:
Ride report:	Ride report:
RPE: 1 – 10	RPE: 1 – 10

THURSDAY			
Energy	Sleep (hrs)	Sleep quality	Stress
Mood	Weather	Soreness	Weight
Injury/illness			

Ride 1	Ride 2
Resting heart rate:	Resting heart rate:
Route:	Route:
Distance:	Distance:
Time:	Time:
Zone: 1 2 3 4 5	Zone: 1 2 3 4 5
Average speed:	Average speed:
Max speed:	Max speed:
Inclination:	Inclination:
Food and water intake:	Food and water intake:
Ride report:	Ride report:
RPE: 1 – 10	RPE: 1 – 10

Week Beginning / / Continued

FRIDAY			
Energy	Sleep (hrs)	Sleep quality	Stress
Mood	Weather	Soreness	Weight
Injury/illness			

Ride 1	Ride 2
Resting heart rate:	Resting heart rate:
Route:	Route:
Distance:	Distance:
Time:	Time:
Zone: 1 2 3 4 5	Zone: 1 2 3 4 5
Average speed:	Average speed:
Max speed:	Max speed:
Inclination:	Inclination:
Food and water intake:	Food and water intake:
Ride report:	Ride report:
RPE: 1 – 10	RPE: 1 – 10

SATURDAY			
Energy	Sleep (hrs)	Sleep quality	Stress
Mood	Weather	Soreness	Weight
Injury/illness			

Ride 1	Ride 2
Resting heart rate:	Resting heart rate:
Route:	Route:
Distance:	Distance:
Time:	Time:
Zone: 1 2 3 4 5	Zone: 1 2 3 4 5
Average speed:	Average speed:
Max speed:	Max speed:
Inclination:	Inclination:
Food and water intake:	Food and water intake:
Ride report:	Ride report:
RPE: 1 – 10	RPE: 1 – 10

SUNDAY

Energy		Sleep (hrs)		Sleep quality		Stress	
Mood		Weather		Soreness		Weight	

Injury/illness

Ride 1	Ride 2
Resting heart rate:	Resting heart rate:
Route:	Route:
Distance:	Distance:
Time:	Time:
Zone: 1 2 3 4 5	Zone: 1 2 3 4 5
Average speed:	Average speed:
Max speed:	Max speed:
Inclination:	Inclination:
Food and water intake:	Food and water intake:
Ride report:	Ride report:
RPE: 1 – 10	RPE: 1 – 10

WEEKLY COMPETITION

Race 1	Race 2
Time Goal:	Time Goal:
Resting heart rate:	Resting heart rate:
Weather:	Weather:
Route:	Route:
Distance:	Distance:
Time:	Time:
Zone: 1 2 3 4 5	Zone: 1 2 3 4 5
Average speed:	Average speed:
Inclination:	Inclination:
Notes:	Notes:

WEEKLY SUMMARY

Weight		Distance		Time	
Average speed		RPE: 1 – 10			
Notes:					

Week Beginning

 / /

MONDAY			
Energy	Sleep (hrs)	Sleep quality	Stress
Mood	Weather	Soreness	Weight
Injury/illness			

Ride 1	Ride 2
Resting heart rate:	Resting heart rate:
Route:	Route:
Distance:	Distance:
Time:	Time:
Zone: 1 2 3 4 5	Zone: 1 2 3 4 5
Average speed:	Average speed:
Max speed:	Max speed:
Inclination:	Inclination:
Food and water intake:	Food and water intake:
Ride report:	Ride report:
RPE: 1 – 10	RPE: 1 – 10

TUESDAY			
Energy	Sleep (hrs)	Sleep quality	Stress
Mood	Weather	Soreness	Weight
Injury/illness			

Ride 1	Ride 2
Resting heart rate:	Resting heart rate:
Route:	Route:
Distance:	Distance:
Time:	Time:
Zone: 1 2 3 4 5	Zone: 1 2 3 4 5
Average speed:	Average speed:
Max speed:	Max speed:
Inclination:	Inclination:
Food and water intake:	Food and water intake:
Ride report:	Ride report:
RPE: 1 – 10	RPE: 1 – 10

Weekly Goals

WEDNESDAY			
Energy	Sleep (hrs)	Sleep quality	Stress
Mood	Weather	Soreness	Weight
Injury/illness			

Ride 1		Ride 2	
Resting heart rate:		Resting heart rate:	
Route:		Route:	
Distance:		Distance:	
Time:		Time:	
Zone: 1 2 3 4 5		Zone: 1 2 3 4 5	
Average speed:		Average speed:	
Max speed:		Max speed:	
Inclination:		Inclination:	
Food and water intake:		Food and water intake:	
Ride report:		Ride report:	
RPE: 1 – 10		RPE: 1 – 10	

THURSDAY			
Energy	Sleep (hrs)	Sleep quality	Stress
Mood	Weather	Soreness	Weight
Injury/illness			

Ride 1		Ride 2	
Resting heart rate:		Resting heart rate:	
Route:		Route:	
Distance:		Distance:	
Time:		Time:	
Zone: 1 2 3 4 5		Zone: 1 2 3 4 5	
Average speed:		Average speed:	
Max speed:		Max speed:	
Inclination:		Inclination:	
Food and water intake:		Food and water intake:	
Ride report:		Ride report:	
RPE: 1 – 10		RPE: 1 – 10	

Week Beginning / / Continued

FRIDAY			
Energy	Sleep (hrs)	Sleep quality	Stress
Mood	Weather	Soreness	Weight
Injury/illness			

Ride 1	Ride 2
Resting heart rate:	Resting heart rate:
Route:	Route:
Distance:	Distance:
Time:	Time:
Zone: 1 2 3 4 5	Zone: 1 2 3 4 5
Average speed:	Average speed:
Max speed:	Max speed:
Inclination:	Inclination:
Food and water intake:	Food and water intake:
Ride report:	Ride report:
RPE: 1 – 10	RPE: 1 – 10

SATURDAY			
Energy	Sleep (hrs)	Sleep quality	Stress
Mood	Weather	Soreness	Weight
Injury/illness			

Ride 1	Ride 2
Resting heart rate:	Resting heart rate:
Route:	Route:
Distance:	Distance:
Time:	Time:
Zone: 1 2 3 4 5	Zone: 1 2 3 4 5
Average speed:	Average speed:
Max speed:	Max speed:
Inclination:	Inclination:
Food and water intake:	Food and water intake:
Ride report:	Ride report:
RPE: 1 – 10	RPE: 1 – 10

SUNDAY			
Energy	Sleep (hrs)	Sleep quality	Stress
Mood	Weather	Soreness	Weight
Injury/illness			

Ride 1	Ride 2
Resting heart rate:	Resting heart rate:
Route:	Route:
Distance:	Distance:
Time:	Time:
Zone: 1 2 3 4 5	Zone: 1 2 3 4 5
Average speed:	Average speed:
Max speed:	Max speed:
Inclination:	Inclination:
Food and water intake:	Food and water intake:
Ride report:	Ride report:
RPE: 1 – 10	RPE: 1 – 10

WEEKLY COMPETITION	
Race 1	Race 2
Time Goal:	Time Goal:
Resting heart rate:	Resting heart rate:
Weather:	Weather:
Route:	Route:
Distance:	Distance:
Time:	Time:
Zone: 1 2 3 4 5	Zone: 1 2 3 4 5
Average speed:	Average speed:
Inclination:	Inclination:
Notes:	Notes:

WEEKLY SUMMARY			
Weight	Distance		Time
Average speed		RPE: 1 – 10	
Notes:			

Week Beginning

 / /

MONDAY			
Energy	Sleep (hrs)	Sleep quality	Stress
Mood	Weather	Soreness	Weight
Injury/illness			

Ride 1	Ride 2
Resting heart rate:	Resting heart rate:
Route:	Route:
Distance:	Distance:
Time:	Time:
Zone: 1 2 3 4 5	Zone: 1 2 3 4 5
Average speed:	Average speed:
Max speed:	Max speed:
Inclination:	Inclination:
Food and water intake:	Food and water intake:
Ride report:	Ride report:
RPE: 1 – 10	RPE: 1 – 10

TUESDAY			
Energy	Sleep (hrs)	Sleep quality	Stress
Mood	Weather	Soreness	Weight
Injury/illness			

Ride 1	Ride 2
Resting heart rate:	Resting heart rate:
Route:	Route:
Distance:	Distance:
Time:	Time:
Zone: 1 2 3 4 5	Zone: 1 2 3 4 5
Average speed:	Average speed:
Max speed:	Max speed:
Inclination:	Inclination:
Food and water intake:	Food and water intake:
Ride report:	Ride report:
RPE: 1 – 10	RPE: 1 – 10

Weekly Goals

WEDNESDAY			
Energy	Sleep (hrs)	Sleep quality	Stress
Mood	Weather	Soreness	Weight
Injury/illness			

Ride 1	Ride 2
Resting heart rate:	Resting heart rate:
Route:	Route:
Distance:	Distance:
Time:	Time:
Zone: 1 2 3 4 5	Zone: 1 2 3 4 5
Average speed:	Average speed:
Max speed:	Max speed:
Inclination:	Inclination:
Food and water intake:	Food and water intake:
Ride report:	Ride report:
RPE: 1 – 10	RPE: 1 – 10

THURSDAY			
Energy	Sleep (hrs)	Sleep quality	Stress
Mood	Weather	Soreness	Weight
Injury/illness			

Ride 1	Ride 2
Resting heart rate:	Resting heart rate:
Route:	Route:
Distance:	Distance:
Time:	Time:
Zone: 1 2 3 4 5	Zone: 1 2 3 4 5
Average speed:	Average speed:
Max speed:	Max speed:
Inclination:	Inclination:
Food and water intake:	Food and water intake:
Ride report:	Ride report:
RPE: 1 – 10	RPE: 1 – 10

Week Beginning  Continued

FRIDAY			
Energy	Sleep (hrs)	Sleep quality	Stress
Mood	Weather	Soreness	Weight
Injury/illness			

Ride 1	Ride 2
Resting heart rate:	Resting heart rate:
Route:	Route:
Distance:	Distance:
Time:	Time:
Zone: 1 2 3 4 5	Zone: 1 2 3 4 5
Average speed:	Average speed:
Max speed:	Max speed:
Inclination:	Inclination:
Food and water intake:	Food and water intake:
Ride report:	Ride report:
RPE: 1 – 10	RPE: 1 – 10

SATURDAY			
Energy	Sleep (hrs)	Sleep quality	Stress
Mood	Weather	Soreness	Weight
Injury/illness			

Ride 1	Ride 2
Resting heart rate:	Resting heart rate:
Route:	Route:
Distance:	Distance:
Time:	Time:
Zone: 1 2 3 4 5	Zone: 1 2 3 4 5
Average speed:	Average speed:
Max speed:	Max speed:
Inclination:	Inclination:
Food and water intake:	Food and water intake:
Ride report:	Ride report:
RPE: 1 – 10	RPE: 1 – 10

SUNDAY			
Energy	Sleep (hrs)	Sleep quality	Stress
Mood	Weather	Soreness	Weight
Injury/illness			

Ride 1	Ride 2
Resting heart rate:	Resting heart rate:
Route:	Route:
Distance:	Distance:
Time:	Time:
Zone: 1 2 3 4 5	Zone: 1 2 3 4 5
Average speed:	Average speed:
Max speed:	Max speed:
Inclination:	Inclination:
Food and water intake:	Food and water intake:
Ride report:	Ride report:
RPE: 1 – 10	RPE: 1 – 10

WEEKLY COMPETITION	
Race 1	Race 2
Time Goal:	Time Goal:
Resting heart rate:	Resting heart rate:
Weather:	Weather:
Route:	Route:
Distance:	Distance:
Time:	Time:
Zone: 1 2 3 4 5	Zone: 1 2 3 4 5
Average speed:	Average speed:
Inclination:	Inclination:
Notes:	Notes:

WEEKLY SUMMARY		
Weight	Distance	Time
Average speed	RPE: 1 – 10	
Notes:		

Week Beginning

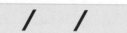

/ /

MONDAY			
Energy	Sleep (hrs)	Sleep quality	Stress
Mood	Weather	Soreness	Weight
Injury/illness			

Ride 1	Ride 2
Resting heart rate:	Resting heart rate:
Route:	Route:
Distance:	Distance:
Time:	Time:
Zone: 1 2 3 4 5	Zone: 1 2 3 4 5
Average speed:	Average speed:
Max speed:	Max speed:
Inclination:	Inclination:
Food and water intake:	Food and water intake:
Ride report:	Ride report:
RPE: 1 – 10	RPE: 1 – 10

TUESDAY			
Energy	Sleep (hrs)	Sleep quality	Stress
Mood	Weather	Soreness	Weight
Injury/illness			

Ride 1	Ride 2
Resting heart rate:	Resting heart rate:
Route:	Route:
Distance:	Distance:
Time:	Time:
Zone: 1 2 3 4 5	Zone: 1 2 3 4 5
Average speed:	Average speed:
Max speed:	Max speed:
Inclination:	Inclination:
Food and water intake:	Food and water intake:
Ride report:	Ride report:
RPE: 1 – 10	RPE: 1 – 10

Weekly Goals

WEDNESDAY			
Energy	Sleep (hrs)	Sleep quality	Stress
Mood	Weather	Soreness	Weight
Injury/illness			

Ride 1		Ride 2	
Resting heart rate:		Resting heart rate:	
Route:		Route:	
Distance:		Distance:	
Time:		Time:	
Zone: 1 2 3 4 5		Zone: 1 2 3 4 5	
Average speed:		Average speed:	
Max speed:		Max speed:	
Inclination:		Inclination:	
Food and water intake:		Food and water intake:	
Ride report:		Ride report:	
RPE: 1 – 10		RPE: 1 – 10	

THURSDAY			
Energy	Sleep (hrs)	Sleep quality	Stress
Mood	Weather	Soreness	Weight
Injury/illness			

Ride 1		Ride 2	
Resting heart rate:		Resting heart rate:	
Route:		Route:	
Distance:		Distance:	
Time:		Time:	
Zone: 1 2 3 4 5		Zone: 1 2 3 4 5	
Average speed:		Average speed:	
Max speed:		Max speed:	
Inclination:		Inclination:	
Food and water intake:		Food and water intake:	
Ride report:		Ride report:	
RPE: 1 – 10		RPE: 1 – 10	

FRIDAY			
Energy	Sleep (hrs)	Sleep quality	Stress
Mood	Weather	Soreness	Weight
Injury/illness			

Ride 1	Ride 2
Resting heart rate:	Resting heart rate:
Route:	Route:
Distance:	Distance:
Time:	Time:
Zone: 1 2 3 4 5	Zone: 1 2 3 4 5
Average speed:	Average speed:
Max speed:	Max speed:
Inclination:	Inclination:
Food and water intake:	Food and water intake:
Ride report:	Ride report:
RPE: 1 – 10	RPE: 1 – 10

SATURDAY			
Energy	Sleep (hrs)	Sleep quality	Stress
Mood	Weather	Soreness	Weight
Injury/illness			

Ride 1	Ride 2
Resting heart rate:	Resting heart rate:
Route:	Route:
Distance:	Distance:
Time:	Time:
Zone: 1 2 3 4 5	Zone: 1 2 3 4 5
Average speed:	Average speed:
Max speed:	Max speed:
Inclination:	Inclination:
Food and water intake:	Food and water intake:
Ride report:	Ride report:
RPE: 1 – 10	RPE: 1 – 10

SUNDAY			
Energy	Sleep (hrs)	Sleep quality	Stress
Mood	Weather	Soreness	Weight
Injury/illness			

Ride 1	Ride 2
Resting heart rate:	Resting heart rate:
Route:	Route:
Distance:	Distance:
Time:	Time:
Zone: 1 2 3 4 5	Zone: 1 2 3 4 5
Average speed:	Average speed:
Max speed:	Max speed:
Inclination:	Inclination:
Food and water intake:	Food and water intake:
Ride report:	Ride report:
RPE: 1 – 10	RPE: 1 – 10

WEEKLY COMPETITION	
Race 1	Race 2
Time Goal:	Time Goal:
Resting heart rate:	Resting heart rate:
Weather:	Weather:
Route:	Route:
Distance:	Distance:
Time:	Time:
Zone: 1 2 3 4 5	Zone: 1 2 3 4 5
Average speed:	Average speed:
Inclination:	Inclination:
Notes:	Notes:

WEEKLY SUMMARY			
Weight	Distance		Time
Average speed		RPE: 1 – 10	
Notes:			

Week Beginning

MONDAY			
Energy	Sleep (hrs)	Sleep quality	Stress
Mood	Weather	Soreness	Weight
Injury/illness			

Ride 1	Ride 2
Resting heart rate:	Resting heart rate:
Route:	Route:
Distance:	Distance:
Time:	Time:
Zone: 1 2 3 4 5	Zone: 1 2 3 4 5
Average speed:	Average speed:
Max speed:	Max speed:
Inclination:	Inclination:
Food and water intake:	Food and water intake:
Ride report:	Ride report:
RPE: 1 – 10	RPE: 1 – 10

TUESDAY			
Energy	Sleep (hrs)	Sleep quality	Stress
Mood	Weather	Soreness	Weight
Injury/illness			

Ride 1	Ride 2
Resting heart rate:	Resting heart rate:
Route:	Route:
Distance:	Distance:
Time:	Time:
Zone: 1 2 3 4 5	Zone: 1 2 3 4 5
Average speed:	Average speed:
Max speed:	Max speed:
Inclination:	Inclination:
Food and water intake:	Food and water intake:
Ride report:	Ride report:
RPE: 1 – 10	RPE: 1 – 10

Weekly Goals

WEDNESDAY			
Energy	Sleep (hrs)	Sleep quality	Stress
Mood	Weather	Soreness	Weight
Injury/illness			

Ride 1		Ride 2	
Resting heart rate:		Resting heart rate:	
Route:		Route:	
Distance:		Distance:	
Time:		Time:	
Zone: 1 2 3 4 5		Zone: 1 2 3 4 5	
Average speed:		Average speed:	
Max speed:		Max speed:	
Inclination:		Inclination:	
Food and water intake:		Food and water intake:	
Ride report:		Ride report:	
RPE: 1 – 10		RPE: 1 – 10	

THURSDAY			
Energy	Sleep (hrs)	Sleep quality	Stress
Mood	Weather	Soreness	Weight
Injury/illness			

Ride 1		Ride 2	
Resting heart rate:		Resting heart rate:	
Route:		Route:	
Distance:		Distance:	
Time:		Time:	
Zone: 1 2 3 4 5		Zone: 1 2 3 4 5	
Average speed:		Average speed:	
Max speed:		Max speed:	
Inclination:		Inclination:	
Food and water intake:		Food and water intake:	
Ride report:		Ride report:	
RPE: 1 – 10		RPE: 1 – 10	

Week Beginning  / / Continued

FRIDAY			
Energy	Sleep (hrs)	Sleep quality	Stress
Mood	Weather	Soreness	Weight
Injury/illness			

Ride 1	Ride 2
Resting heart rate:	Resting heart rate:
Route:	Route:
Distance:	Distance:
Time:	Time:
Zone: 1 2 3 4 5	Zone: 1 2 3 4 5
Average speed:	Average speed:
Max speed:	Max speed:
Inclination:	Inclination:
Food and water intake:	Food and water intake:
Ride report:	Ride report:
RPE: 1 – 10	RPE: 1 – 10

SATURDAY			
Energy	Sleep (hrs)	Sleep quality	Stress
Mood	Weather	Soreness	Weight
Injury/illness			

Ride 1	Ride 2
Resting heart rate:	Resting heart rate:
Route:	Route:
Distance:	Distance:
Time:	Time:
Zone: 1 2 3 4 5	Zone: 1 2 3 4 5
Average speed:	Average speed:
Max speed:	Max speed:
Inclination:	Inclination:
Food and water intake:	Food and water intake:
Ride report:	Ride report:
RPE: 1 – 10	RPE: 1 – 10

SUNDAY				
Energy	Sleep (hrs)		Sleep quality	Stress
Mood	Weather		Soreness	Weight
Injury/illness				

Ride 1	Ride 2
Resting heart rate:	Resting heart rate:
Route:	Route:
Distance:	Distance:
Time:	Time:
Zone: 1 2 3 4 5	Zone: 1 2 3 4 5
Average speed:	Average speed:
Max speed:	Max speed:
Inclination:	Inclination:
Food and water intake:	Food and water intake:
Ride report:	Ride report:
RPE: 1 – 10	RPE: 1 – 10

WEEKLY COMPETITION	
Race 1	Race 2
Time Goal:	Time Goal:
Resting heart rate:	Resting heart rate:
Weather:	Weather:
Route:	Route:
Distance:	Distance:
Time:	Time:
Zone: 1 2 3 4 5	Zone: 1 2 3 4 5
Average speed:	Average speed:
Inclination:	Inclination:
Notes:	Notes:

WEEKLY SUMMARY			
Weight	Distance		Time
Average speed		RPE: 1 – 10	
Notes:			

Week Beginning

 / /

MONDAY			
Energy	Sleep (hrs)	Sleep quality	Stress
Mood	Weather	Soreness	Weight
Injury/illness			

Ride 1	Ride 2
Resting heart rate:	Resting heart rate:
Route:	Route:
Distance:	Distance:
Time:	Time:
Zone: 1 2 3 4 5	Zone: 1 2 3 4 5
Average speed:	Average speed:
Max speed:	Max speed:
Inclination:	Inclination:
Food and water intake:	Food and water intake:
Ride report:	Ride report:
RPE: 1 – 10	RPE: 1 – 10

TUESDAY			
Energy	Sleep (hrs)	Sleep quality	Stress
Mood	Weather	Soreness	Weight
Injury/illness			

Ride 1	Ride 2
Resting heart rate:	Resting heart rate:
Route:	Route:
Distance:	Distance:
Time:	Time:
Zone: 1 2 3 4 5	Zone: 1 2 3 4 5
Average speed:	Average speed:
Max speed:	Max speed:
Inclination:	Inclination:
Food and water intake:	Food and water intake:
Ride report:	Ride report:
RPE: 1 – 10	RPE: 1 – 10

Weekly Goals

WEDNESDAY			
Energy	Sleep (hrs)	Sleep quality	Stress
Mood	Weather	Soreness	Weight
Injury/illness			

Ride 1	Ride 2
Resting heart rate:	Resting heart rate:
Route:	Route:
Distance:	Distance:
Time:	Time:
Zone: 1 2 3 4 5	Zone: 1 2 3 4 5
Average speed:	Average speed:
Max speed:	Max speed:
Inclination:	Inclination:
Food and water intake:	Food and water intake:
Ride report:	Ride report:
RPE: 1 – 10	RPE: 1 – 10

THURSDAY			
Energy	Sleep (hrs)	Sleep quality	Stress
Mood	Weather	Soreness	Weight
Injury/illness			

Ride 1	Ride 2
Resting heart rate:	Resting heart rate:
Route:	Route:
Distance:	Distance:
Time:	Time:
Zone: 1 2 3 4 5	Zone: 1 2 3 4 5
Average speed:	Average speed:
Max speed:	Max speed:
Inclination:	Inclination:
Food and water intake:	Food and water intake:
Ride report:	Ride report:
RPE: 1 – 10	RPE: 1 – 10

Week Beginning  / / Continued

FRIDAY			
Energy	Sleep (hrs)	Sleep quality	Stress
Mood	Weather	Soreness	Weight
Injury/illness			

Ride 1	Ride 2
Resting heart rate:	Resting heart rate:
Route:	Route:
Distance:	Distance:
Time:	Time:
Zone: 1 2 3 4 5	Zone: 1 2 3 4 5
Average speed:	Average speed:
Max speed:	Max speed:
Inclination:	Inclination:
Food and water intake:	Food and water intake:
Ride report:	Ride report:
RPE: 1 – 10	RPE: 1 – 10

SATURDAY			
Energy	Sleep (hrs)	Sleep quality	Stress
Mood	Weather	Soreness	Weight
Injury/illness			

Ride 1	Ride 2
Resting heart rate:	Resting heart rate:
Route:	Route:
Distance:	Distance:
Time:	Time:
Zone: 1 2 3 4 5	Zone: 1 2 3 4 5
Average speed:	Average speed:
Max speed:	Max speed:
Inclination:	Inclination:
Food and water intake:	Food and water intake:
Ride report:	Ride report:
RPE: 1 – 10	RPE: 1 – 10

SUNDAY

Energy		Sleep (hrs)		Sleep quality		Stress	
Mood		Weather		Soreness		Weight	

Injury/illness

Ride 1	Ride 2
Resting heart rate:	Resting heart rate:
Route:	Route:
Distance:	Distance:
Time:	Time:
Zone: 1 2 3 4 5	Zone: 1 2 3 4 5
Average speed:	Average speed:
Max speed:	Max speed:
Inclination:	Inclination:
Food and water intake:	Food and water intake:
Ride report:	Ride report:
RPE: 1 – 10	RPE: 1 – 10

WEEKLY COMPETITION

Race 1	Race 2
Time Goal:	Time Goal:
Resting heart rate:	Resting heart rate:
Weather:	Weather:
Route:	Route:
Distance:	Distance:
Time:	Time:
Zone: 1 2 3 4 5	Zone: 1 2 3 4 5
Average speed:	Average speed:
Inclination:	Inclination:
Notes:	Notes:

WEEKLY SUMMARY

Weight		Distance		Time	
Average speed		RPE: 1 – 10			
Notes:					

Week Beginning

/ /

MONDAY

Energy		Sleep (hrs)		Sleep quality		Stress	
Mood		Weather		Soreness		Weight	
Injury/illness							

Ride 1				Ride 2			
Resting heart rate:				Resting heart rate:			
Route:				Route:			
Distance:				Distance:			
Time:				Time:			
Zone: 1	2	3	4	5	Zone: 1	2	3	4	5
Average speed:				Average speed:			
Max speed:				Max speed:			
Inclination:				Inclination:			
Food and water intake:				Food and water intake:			
Ride report:				Ride report:			
RPE: 1 – 10				RPE: 1 – 10			

TUESDAY

Energy		Sleep (hrs)		Sleep quality		Stress	
Mood		Weather		Soreness		Weight	
Injury/illness							

Ride 1				Ride 2			
Resting heart rate:				Resting heart rate:			
Route:				Route:			
Distance:				Distance:			
Time:				Time:			
Zone: 1	2	3	4	5	Zone: 1	2	3	4	5
Average speed:				Average speed:			
Max speed:				Max speed:			
Inclination:				Inclination:			
Food and water intake:				Food and water intake:			
Ride report:				Ride report:			
RPE: 1 – 10				RPE: 1 – 10			

Weekly Goals

WEDNESDAY			
Energy	Sleep (hrs)	Sleep quality	Stress
Mood	Weather	Soreness	Weight
Injury/illness			

Ride 1	Ride 2
Resting heart rate:	Resting heart rate:
Route:	Route:
Distance:	Distance:
Time:	Time:
Zone:　1　　2　　3　　4　　5	Zone:　1　　2　　3　　4　　5
Average speed:	Average speed:
Max speed:	Max speed:
Inclination:	Inclination:
Food and water intake:	Food and water intake:
Ride report:	Ride report:
RPE: 1 – 10	RPE: 1 – 10

THURSDAY			
Energy	Sleep (hrs)	Sleep quality	Stress
Mood	Weather	Soreness	Weight
Injury/illness			

Ride 1	Ride 2
Resting heart rate:	Resting heart rate:
Route:	Route:
Distance:	Distance:
Time:	Time:
Zone:　1　　2　　3　　4　　5	Zone:　1　　2　　3　　4　　5
Average speed:	Average speed:
Max speed:	Max speed:
Inclination:	Inclination:
Food and water intake:	Food and water intake:
Ride report:	Ride report:
RPE: 1 – 10	RPE: 1 – 10

FRIDAY			
Energy	Sleep (hrs)	Sleep quality	Stress
Mood	Weather	Soreness	Weight
Injury/illness			

Ride 1		Ride 2	
Resting heart rate:		Resting heart rate:	
Route:		Route:	
Distance:		Distance:	
Time:		Time:	
Zone: 1 2 3 4 5		Zone: 1 2 3 4 5	
Average speed:		Average speed:	
Max speed:		Max speed:	
Inclination:		Inclination:	
Food and water intake:		Food and water intake:	
Ride report:		Ride report:	
RPE: 1 – 10		RPE: 1 – 10	

SATURDAY			
Energy	Sleep (hrs)	Sleep quality	Stress
Mood	Weather	Soreness	Weight
Injury/illness			

Ride 1		Ride 2	
Resting heart rate:		Resting heart rate:	
Route:		Route:	
Distance:		Distance:	
Time:		Time:	
Zone: 1 2 3 4 5		Zone: 1 2 3 4 5	
Average speed:		Average speed:	
Max speed:		Max speed:	
Inclination:		Inclination:	
Food and water intake:		Food and water intake:	
Ride report:		Ride report:	
RPE: 1 – 10		RPE: 1 – 10	

SUNDAY			
Energy	Sleep (hrs)	Sleep quality	Stress
Mood	Weather	Soreness	Weight
Injury/illness			

Ride 1	Ride 2
Resting heart rate:	Resting heart rate:
Route:	Route:
Distance:	Distance:
Time:	Time:
Zone: 1 2 3 4 5	Zone: 1 2 3 4 5
Average speed:	Average speed:
Max speed:	Max speed:
Inclination:	Inclination:
Food and water intake:	Food and water intake:
Ride report:	Ride report:
RPE: 1 – 10	RPE: 1 – 10

WEEKLY COMPETITION	
Race 1	Race 2
Time Goal:	Time Goal:
Resting heart rate:	Resting heart rate:
Weather:	Weather:
Route:	Route:
Distance:	Distance:
Time:	Time:
Zone: 1 2 3 4 5	Zone: 1 2 3 4 5
Average speed:	Average speed:
Inclination:	Inclination:
Notes:	Notes:

WEEKLY SUMMARY		
Weight	Distance	Time
Average speed	RPE: 1 – 10	
Notes:		

Week Beginning

/ /

MONDAY

Energy		Sleep (hrs)		Sleep quality		Stress	
Mood		Weather		Soreness		Weight	
Injury/illness							

Ride 1	Ride 2
Resting heart rate:	Resting heart rate:
Route:	Route:
Distance:	Distance:
Time:	Time:
Zone: 1 2 3 4 5	Zone: 1 2 3 4 5
Average speed:	Average speed:
Max speed:	Max speed:
Inclination:	Inclination:
Food and water intake:	Food and water intake:
Ride report:	Ride report:
RPE: 1 – 10	RPE: 1 – 10

TUESDAY

Energy		Sleep (hrs)		Sleep quality		Stress	
Mood		Weather		Soreness		Weight	
Injury/illness							

Ride 1	Ride 2
Resting heart rate:	Resting heart rate:
Route:	Route:
Distance:	Distance:
Time:	Time:
Zone: 1 2 3 4 5	Zone: 1 2 3 4 5
Average speed:	Average speed:
Max speed:	Max speed:
Inclination:	Inclination:
Food and water intake:	Food and water intake:
Ride report:	Ride report:
RPE: 1 – 10	RPE: 1 – 10

Weekly Goals

WEDNESDAY			
Energy	Sleep (hrs)	Sleep quality	Stress
Mood	Weather	Soreness	Weight
Injury/illness			

Ride 1	Ride 2
Resting heart rate:	Resting heart rate:
Route:	Route:
Distance:	Distance:
Time:	Time:
Zone: 1 2 3 4 5	Zone: 1 2 3 4 5
Average speed:	Average speed:
Max speed:	Max speed:
Inclination:	Inclination:
Food and water intake:	Food and water intake:
Ride report:	Ride report:
RPE: 1 – 10	RPE: 1 – 10

THURSDAY			
Energy	Sleep (hrs)	Sleep quality	Stress
Mood	Weather	Soreness	Weight
Injury/illness			

Ride 1	Ride 2
Resting heart rate:	Resting heart rate:
Route:	Route:
Distance:	Distance:
Time:	Time:
Zone: 1 2 3 4 5	Zone: 1 2 3 4 5
Average speed:	Average speed:
Max speed:	Max speed:
Inclination:	Inclination:
Food and water intake:	Food and water intake:
Ride report:	Ride report:
RPE: 1 – 10	RPE: 1 – 10

FRIDAY			
Energy	Sleep (hrs)	Sleep quality	Stress
Mood	Weather	Soreness	Weight
Injury/illness			

Ride 1	Ride 2
Resting heart rate:	Resting heart rate:
Route:	Route:
Distance:	Distance:
Time:	Time:
Zone: 1 2 3 4 5	Zone: 1 2 3 4 5
Average speed:	Average speed:
Max speed:	Max speed:
Inclination:	Inclination:
Food and water intake:	Food and water intake:
Ride report:	Ride report:
RPE: 1 – 10	RPE: 1 – 10

SATURDAY			
Energy	Sleep (hrs)	Sleep quality	Stress
Mood	Weather	Soreness	Weight
Injury/illness			

Ride 1	Ride 2
Resting heart rate:	Resting heart rate:
Route:	Route:
Distance:	Distance:
Time:	Time:
Zone: 1 2 3 4 5	Zone: 1 2 3 4 5
Average speed:	Average speed:
Max speed:	Max speed:
Inclination:	Inclination:
Food and water intake:	Food and water intake:
Ride report:	Ride report:
RPE: 1 – 10	RPE: 1 – 10

SUNDAY			
Energy	Sleep (hrs)	Sleep quality	Stress
Mood	Weather	Soreness	Weight
Injury/illness			

Ride 1	Ride 2
Resting heart rate:	Resting heart rate:
Route:	Route:
Distance:	Distance:
Time:	Time:
Zone: 1 2 3 4 5	Zone: 1 2 3 4 5
Average speed:	Average speed:
Max speed:	Max speed:
Inclination:	Inclination:
Food and water intake:	Food and water intake:
Ride report:	Ride report:
RPE: 1 – 10	RPE: 1 – 10

WEEKLY COMPETITION	
Race 1	Race 2
Time Goal:	Time Goal:
Resting heart rate:	Resting heart rate:
Weather:	Weather:
Route:	Route:
Distance:	Distance:
Time:	Time:
Zone: 1 2 3 4 5	Zone: 1 2 3 4 5
Average speed:	Average speed:
Inclination:	Inclination:
Notes:	Notes:

WEEKLY SUMMARY		
Weight	Distance	Time
Average speed	RPE: 1 – 10	
Notes:		

Week Beginning

 / /

MONDAY

Energy		Sleep (hrs)		Sleep quality		Stress	
Mood		Weather		Soreness		Weight	

Injury/illness

Ride 1	Ride 2
Resting heart rate:	Resting heart rate:
Route:	Route:
Distance:	Distance:
Time:	Time:
Zone: 1 2 3 4 5	Zone: 1 2 3 4 5
Average speed:	Average speed:
Max speed:	Max speed:
Inclination:	Inclination:
Food and water intake:	Food and water intake:
Ride report:	Ride report:
RPE: 1 – 10	RPE: 1 – 10

TUESDAY

Energy		Sleep (hrs)		Sleep quality		Stress	
Mood		Weather		Soreness		Weight	

Injury/illness

Ride 1	Ride 2
Resting heart rate:	Resting heart rate:
Route:	Route:
Distance:	Distance:
Time:	Time:
Zone: 1 2 3 4 5	Zone: 1 2 3 4 5
Average speed:	Average speed:
Max speed:	Max speed:
Inclination:	Inclination:
Food and water intake:	Food and water intake:
Ride report:	Ride report:
RPE: 1 – 10	RPE: 1 – 10

Weekly Goals

WEDNESDAY			
Energy	Sleep (hrs)	Sleep quality	Stress
Mood	Weather	Soreness	Weight
Injury/illness			

Ride 1	Ride 2
Resting heart rate:	Resting heart rate:
Route:	Route:
Distance:	Distance:
Time:	Time:
Zone: 1 2 3 4 5	Zone: 1 2 3 4 5
Average speed:	Average speed:
Max speed:	Max speed:
Inclination:	Inclination:
Food and water intake:	Food and water intake:
Ride report:	Ride report:
RPE: 1 – 10	RPE: 1 – 10

THURSDAY			
Energy	Sleep (hrs)	Sleep quality	Stress
Mood	Weather	Soreness	Weight
Injury/illness			

Ride 1	Ride 2
Resting heart rate:	Resting heart rate:
Route:	Route:
Distance:	Distance:
Time:	Time:
Zone: 1 2 3 4 5	Zone: 1 2 3 4 5
Average speed:	Average speed:
Max speed:	Max speed:
Inclination:	Inclination:
Food and water intake:	Food and water intake:
Ride report:	Ride report:
RPE: 1 – 10	RPE: 1 – 10

Week Beginning / / Continued

FRIDAY			
Energy	Sleep (hrs)	Sleep quality	Stress
Mood	Weather	Soreness	Weight
Injury/illness			

Ride 1	Ride 2
Resting heart rate:	Resting heart rate:
Route:	Route:
Distance:	Distance:
Time:	Time:
Zone: 1 2 3 4 5	Zone: 1 2 3 4 5
Average speed:	Average speed:
Max speed:	Max speed:
Inclination:	Inclination:
Food and water intake:	Food and water intake:
Ride report:	Ride report:
RPE: 1 – 10	RPE: 1 – 10

SATURDAY			
Energy	Sleep (hrs)	Sleep quality	Stress
Mood	Weather	Soreness	Weight
Injury/illness			

Ride 1	Ride 2
Resting heart rate:	Resting heart rate:
Route:	Route:
Distance:	Distance:
Time:	Time:
Zone: 1 2 3 4 5	Zone: 1 2 3 4 5
Average speed:	Average speed:
Max speed:	Max speed:
Inclination:	Inclination:
Food and water intake:	Food and water intake:
Ride report:	Ride report:
RPE: 1 – 10	RPE: 1 – 10

SUNDAY			
Energy	Sleep (hrs)	Sleep quality	Stress
Mood	Weather	Soreness	Weight
Injury/illness			

Ride 1	Ride 2
Resting heart rate:	Resting heart rate:
Route:	Route:
Distance:	Distance:
Time:	Time:
Zone: 1 2 3 4 5	Zone: 1 2 3 4 5
Average speed:	Average speed:
Max speed:	Max speed:
Inclination:	Inclination:
Food and water intake:	Food and water intake:
Ride report:	Ride report:
RPE: 1 – 10	RPE: 1 – 10

WEEKLY COMPETITION	
Race 1	Race 2
Time Goal:	Time Goal:
Resting heart rate:	Resting heart rate:
Weather:	Weather:
Route:	Route:
Distance:	Distance:
Time:	Time:
Zone: 1 2 3 4 5	Zone: 1 2 3 4 5
Average speed:	Average speed:
Inclination:	Inclination:
Notes:	Notes:

WEEKLY SUMMARY			
Weight	Distance		Time
Average speed	RPE: 1 – 10		
Notes:			

Week Beginning

/ /

MONDAY			
Energy	Sleep (hrs)	Sleep quality	Stress
Mood	Weather	Soreness	Weight
Injury/illness			

Ride 1	Ride 2
Resting heart rate:	Resting heart rate:
Route:	Route:
Distance:	Distance:
Time:	Time:
Zone: 1 2 3 4 5	Zone: 1 2 3 4 5
Average speed:	Average speed:
Max speed:	Max speed:
Inclination:	Inclination:
Food and water intake:	Food and water intake:
Ride report:	Ride report:
RPE: 1 – 10	RPE: 1 – 10

TUESDAY			
Energy	Sleep (hrs)	Sleep quality	Stress
Mood	Weather	Soreness	Weight
Injury/illness			

Ride 1	Ride 2
Resting heart rate:	Resting heart rate:
Route:	Route:
Distance:	Distance:
Time:	Time:
Zone: 1 2 3 4 5	Zone: 1 2 3 4 5
Average speed:	Average speed:
Max speed:	Max speed:
Inclination:	Inclination:
Food and water intake:	Food and water intake:
Ride report:	Ride report:
RPE: 1 – 10	RPE: 1 – 10

Weekly Goals

WEDNESDAY			
Energy	Sleep (hrs)	Sleep quality	Stress
Mood	Weather	Soreness	Weight
Injury/illness			

Ride 1	Ride 2
Resting heart rate:	Resting heart rate:
Route:	Route:
Distance:	Distance:
Time:	Time:
Zone: 1 2 3 4 5	Zone: 1 2 3 4 5
Average speed:	Average speed:
Max speed:	Max speed:
Inclination:	Inclination:
Food and water intake:	Food and water intake:
Ride report:	Ride report:
RPE: 1 – 10	RPE: 1 – 10

THURSDAY			
Energy	Sleep (hrs)	Sleep quality	Stress
Mood	Weather	Soreness	Weight
Injury/illness			

Ride 1	Ride 2
Resting heart rate:	Resting heart rate:
Route:	Route:
Distance:	Distance:
Time:	Time:
Zone: 1 2 3 4 5	Zone: 1 2 3 4 5
Average speed:	Average speed:
Max speed:	Max speed:
Inclination:	Inclination:
Food and water intake:	Food and water intake:
Ride report:	Ride report:
RPE: 1 – 10	RPE: 1 – 10

FRIDAY			
Energy	Sleep (hrs)	Sleep quality	Stress
Mood	Weather	Soreness	Weight
Injury/illness			

Ride 1	Ride 2
Resting heart rate:	Resting heart rate:
Route:	Route:
Distance:	Distance:
Time:	Time:
Zone: 1 2 3 4 5	Zone: 1 2 3 4 5
Average speed:	Average speed:
Max speed:	Max speed:
Inclination:	Inclination:
Food and water intake:	Food and water intake:
Ride report:	Ride report:
RPE: 1 – 10	RPE: 1 – 10

SATURDAY			
Energy	Sleep (hrs)	Sleep quality	Stress
Mood	Weather	Soreness	Weight
Injury/illness			

Ride 1	Ride 2
Resting heart rate:	Resting heart rate:
Route:	Route:
Distance:	Distance:
Time:	Time:
Zone: 1 2 3 4 5	Zone: 1 2 3 4 5
Average speed:	Average speed:
Max speed:	Max speed:
Inclination:	Inclination:
Food and water intake:	Food and water intake:
Ride report:	Ride report:
RPE: 1 – 10	RPE: 1 – 10

SUNDAY			
Energy	Sleep (hrs)	Sleep quality	Stress
Mood	Weather	Soreness	Weight
Injury/illness			

Ride 1	Ride 2
Resting heart rate:	Resting heart rate:
Route:	Route:
Distance:	Distance:
Time:	Time:
Zone: 1 2 3 4 5	Zone: 1 2 3 4 5
Average speed:	Average speed:
Max speed:	Max speed:
Inclination:	Inclination:
Food and water intake:	Food and water intake:
Ride report:	Ride report:
RPE: 1 – 10	RPE: 1 – 10

WEEKLY COMPETITION	
Race 1	Race 2
Time Goal:	Time Goal:
Resting heart rate:	Resting heart rate:
Weather:	Weather:
Route:	Route:
Distance:	Distance:
Time:	Time:
Zone: 1 2 3 4 5	Zone: 1 2 3 4 5
Average speed:	Average speed:
Inclination:	Inclination:
Notes:	Notes:

WEEKLY SUMMARY			
Weight	Distance		Time
Average speed		RPE: 1 – 10	
Notes:			

Week Beginning

/ /

MONDAY			
Energy	Sleep (hrs)	Sleep quality	Stress
Mood	Weather	Soreness	Weight
Injury/illness			

Ride 1	Ride 2
Resting heart rate:	Resting heart rate:
Route:	Route:
Distance:	Distance:
Time:	Time:
Zone: 1 2 3 4 5	Zone: 1 2 3 4 5
Average speed:	Average speed:
Max speed:	Max speed:
Inclination:	Inclination:
Food and water intake:	Food and water intake:
Ride report:	Ride report:
RPE: 1 – 10	RPE: 1 – 10

TUESDAY			
Energy	Sleep (hrs)	Sleep quality	Stress
Mood	Weather	Soreness	Weight
Injury/illness			

Ride 1	Ride 2
Resting heart rate:	Resting heart rate:
Route:	Route:
Distance:	Distance:
Time:	Time:
Zone: 1 2 3 4 5	Zone: 1 2 3 4 5
Average speed:	Average speed:
Max speed:	Max speed:
Inclination:	Inclination:
Food and water intake:	Food and water intake:
Ride report:	Ride report:
RPE: 1 – 10	RPE: 1 – 10

Weekly Goals

WEDNESDAY			
Energy	Sleep (hrs)	Sleep quality	Stress
Mood	Weather	Soreness	Weight
Injury/illness			

Ride 1	Ride 2
Resting heart rate:	Resting heart rate:
Route:	Route:
Distance:	Distance:
Time:	Time:
Zone: 1 2 3 4 5	Zone: 1 2 3 4 5
Average speed:	Average speed:
Max speed:	Max speed:
Inclination:	Inclination:
Food and water intake:	Food and water intake:
Ride report:	Ride report:
RPE: 1 – 10	RPE: 1 – 10

THURSDAY			
Energy	Sleep (hrs)	Sleep quality	Stress
Mood	Weather	Soreness	Weight
Injury/illness			

Ride 1	Ride 2
Resting heart rate:	Resting heart rate:
Route:	Route:
Distance:	Distance:
Time:	Time:
Zone: 1 2 3 4 5	Zone: 1 2 3 4 5
Average speed:	Average speed:
Max speed:	Max speed:
Inclination:	Inclination:
Food and water intake:	Food and water intake:
Ride report:	Ride report:
RPE: 1 – 10	RPE: 1 – 10

Week Beginning  / / Continued

FRIDAY			
Energy	Sleep (hrs)	Sleep quality	Stress
Mood	Weather	Soreness	Weight
Injury/illness			

Ride 1	Ride 2
Resting heart rate:	Resting heart rate:
Route:	Route:
Distance:	Distance:
Time:	Time:
Zone: 1 2 3 4 5	Zone: 1 2 3 4 5
Average speed:	Average speed:
Max speed:	Max speed:
Inclination:	Inclination:
Food and water intake:	Food and water intake:
Ride report:	Ride report:
RPE: 1 – 10	RPE: 1 – 10

SATURDAY			
Energy	Sleep (hrs)	Sleep quality	Stress
Mood	Weather	Soreness	Weight
Injury/illness			

Ride 1	Ride 2
Resting heart rate:	Resting heart rate:
Route:	Route:
Distance:	Distance:
Time:	Time:
Zone: 1 2 3 4 5	Zone: 1 2 3 4 5
Average speed:	Average speed:
Max speed:	Max speed:
Inclination:	Inclination:
Food and water intake:	Food and water intake:
Ride report:	Ride report:
RPE: 1 – 10	RPE: 1 – 10

SUNDAY

Energy		Sleep (hrs)		Sleep quality		Stress	
Mood		Weather		Soreness		Weight	
Injury/illness							

Ride 1	Ride 2
Resting heart rate:	Resting heart rate:
Route:	Route:
Distance:	Distance:
Time:	Time:
Zone: 1 2 3 4 5	Zone: 1 2 3 4 5
Average speed:	Average speed:
Max speed:	Max speed:
Inclination:	Inclination:
Food and water intake:	Food and water intake:
Ride report:	Ride report:
RPE: 1 – 10	RPE: 1 – 10

WEEKLY COMPETITION

Race 1	Race 2
Time Goal:	Time Goal:
Resting heart rate:	Resting heart rate:
Weather:	Weather:
Route:	Route:
Distance:	Distance:
Time:	Time:
Zone: 1 2 3 4 5	Zone: 1 2 3 4 5
Average speed:	Average speed:
Inclination:	Inclination:
Notes:	Notes:

WEEKLY SUMMARY

Weight		Distance		Time	
Average speed		RPE: 1 – 10			
Notes:					

Week Beginning

/ /

MONDAY			
Energy	Sleep (hrs)	Sleep quality	Stress
Mood	Weather	Soreness	Weight
Injury/illness			

Ride 1	Ride 2
Resting heart rate:	Resting heart rate:
Route:	Route:
Distance:	Distance:
Time:	Time:
Zone: 1　2　3　4　5	Zone: 1　2　3　4　5
Average speed:	Average speed:
Max speed:	Max speed:
Inclination:	Inclination:
Food and water intake:	Food and water intake:
Ride report:	Ride report:
RPE: 1 – 10	RPE: 1 – 10

TUESDAY			
Energy	Sleep (hrs)	Sleep quality	Stress
Mood	Weather	Soreness	Weight
Injury/illness			

Ride 1	Ride 2
Resting heart rate:	Resting heart rate:
Route:	Route:
Distance:	Distance:
Time:	Time:
Zone: 1　2　3　4　5	Zone: 1　2　3　4　5
Average speed:	Average speed:
Max speed:	Max speed:
Inclination:	Inclination:
Food and water intake:	Food and water intake:
Ride report:	Ride report:
RPE: 1 – 10	RPE: 1 – 10

Weekly Goals

WEDNESDAY			
Energy	Sleep (hrs)	Sleep quality	Stress
Mood	Weather	Soreness	Weight
Injury/illness			

Ride 1	Ride 2
Resting heart rate:	Resting heart rate:
Route:	Route:
Distance:	Distance:
Time:	Time:
Zone: 1 2 3 4 5	Zone: 1 2 3 4 5
Average speed:	Average speed:
Max speed:	Max speed:
Inclination:	Inclination:
Food and water intake:	Food and water intake:
Ride report:	Ride report:
RPE: 1 – 10	RPE: 1 – 10

THURSDAY			
Energy	Sleep (hrs)	Sleep quality	Stress
Mood	Weather	Soreness	Weight
Injury/illness			

Ride 1	Ride 2
Resting heart rate:	Resting heart rate:
Route:	Route:
Distance:	Distance:
Time:	Time:
Zone: 1 2 3 4 5	Zone: 1 2 3 4 5
Average speed:	Average speed:
Max speed:	Max speed:
Inclination:	Inclination:
Food and water intake:	Food and water intake:
Ride report:	Ride report:
RPE: 1 – 10	RPE: 1 – 10

FRIDAY			
Energy	Sleep (hrs)	Sleep quality	Stress
Mood	Weather	Soreness	Weight
Injury/illness			

Ride 1	Ride 2
Resting heart rate:	Resting heart rate:
Route:	Route:
Distance:	Distance:
Time:	Time:
Zone: 1 2 3 4 5	Zone: 1 2 3 4 5
Average speed:	Average speed:
Max speed:	Max speed:
Inclination:	Inclination:
Food and water intake:	Food and water intake:
Ride report:	Ride report:
RPE: 1 – 10	RPE: 1 – 10

SATURDAY			
Energy	Sleep (hrs)	Sleep quality	Stress
Mood	Weather	Soreness	Weight
Injury/illness			

Ride 1	Ride 2
Resting heart rate:	Resting heart rate:
Route:	Route:
Distance:	Distance:
Time:	Time:
Zone: 1 2 3 4 5	Zone: 1 2 3 4 5
Average speed:	Average speed:
Max speed:	Max speed:
Inclination:	Inclination:
Food and water intake:	Food and water intake:
Ride report:	Ride report:
RPE: 1 – 10	RPE: 1 – 10

SUNDAY			
Energy	Sleep (hrs)	Sleep quality	Stress
Mood	Weather	Soreness	Weight
Injury/illness			

Ride 1	Ride 2
Resting heart rate:	Resting heart rate:
Route:	Route:
Distance:	Distance:
Time:	Time:
Zone: 1 2 3 4 5	Zone: 1 2 3 4 5
Average speed:	Average speed:
Max speed:	Max speed:
Inclination:	Inclination:
Food and water intake:	Food and water intake:
Ride report:	Ride report:
RPE: 1 – 10	RPE: 1 – 10

WEEKLY COMPETITION	
Race 1	Race 2
Time Goal:	Time Goal:
Resting heart rate:	Resting heart rate:
Weather:	Weather:
Route:	Route:
Distance:	Distance:
Time:	Time:
Zone: 1 2 3 4 5	Zone: 1 2 3 4 5
Average speed:	Average speed:
Inclination:	Inclination:
Notes:	Notes:

WEEKLY SUMMARY			
Weight	Distance		Time
Average speed		RPE: 1 – 10	
Notes:			

Week Beginning

/   /

MONDAY			
Energy	Sleep (hrs)	Sleep quality	Stress
Mood	Weather	Soreness	Weight
Injury/illness			

Ride 1	Ride 2
Resting heart rate:	Resting heart rate:
Route:	Route:
Distance:	Distance:
Time:	Time:
Zone: 1 2 3 4 5	Zone: 1 2 3 4 5
Average speed:	Average speed:
Max speed:	Max speed:
Inclination:	Inclination:
Food and water intake:	Food and water intake:
Ride report:	Ride report:
RPE: 1 – 10	RPE: 1 – 10

TUESDAY			
Energy	Sleep (hrs)	Sleep quality	Stress
Mood	Weather	Soreness	Weight
Injury/illness			

Ride 1	Ride 2
Resting heart rate:	Resting heart rate:
Route:	Route:
Distance:	Distance:
Time:	Time:
Zone: 1 2 3 4 5	Zone: 1 2 3 4 5
Average speed:	Average speed:
Max speed:	Max speed:
Inclination:	Inclination:
Food and water intake:	Food and water intake:
Ride report:	Ride report:
RPE: 1 – 10	RPE: 1 – 10

Weekly Goals

WEDNESDAY			
Energy	Sleep (hrs)	Sleep quality	Stress
Mood	Weather	Soreness	Weight
Injury/illness			

Ride 1		Ride 2	
Resting heart rate:		Resting heart rate:	
Route:		Route:	
Distance:		Distance:	
Time:		Time:	
Zone: 1 2 3 4 5		Zone: 1 2 3 4 5	
Average speed:		Average speed:	
Max speed:		Max speed:	
Inclination:		Inclination:	
Food and water intake:		Food and water intake:	
Ride report:		Ride report:	
RPE: 1 – 10		RPE: 1 – 10	

THURSDAY			
Energy	Sleep (hrs)	Sleep quality	Stress
Mood	Weather	Soreness	Weight
Injury/illness			

Ride 1		Ride 2	
Resting heart rate:		Resting heart rate:	
Route:		Route:	
Distance:		Distance:	
Time:		Time:	
Zone: 1 2 3 4 5		Zone: 1 2 3 4 5	
Average speed:		Average speed:	
Max speed:		Max speed:	
Inclination:		Inclination:	
Food and water intake:		Food and water intake:	
Ride report:		Ride report:	
RPE: 1 – 10		RPE: 1 – 10	

FRIDAY			
Energy	Sleep (hrs)	Sleep quality	Stress
Mood	Weather	Soreness	Weight
Injury/illness			

Ride 1	Ride 2
Resting heart rate:	Resting heart rate:
Route:	Route:
Distance:	Distance:
Time:	Time:
Zone: 1 2 3 4 5	Zone: 1 2 3 4 5
Average speed:	Average speed:
Max speed:	Max speed:
Inclination:	Inclination:
Food and water intake:	Food and water intake:
Ride report:	Ride report:
RPE: 1 – 10	RPE: 1 – 10

SATURDAY			
Energy	Sleep (hrs)	Sleep quality	Stress
Mood	Weather	Soreness	Weight
Injury/illness			

Ride 1	Ride 2
Resting heart rate:	Resting heart rate:
Route:	Route:
Distance:	Distance:
Time:	Time:
Zone: 1 2 3 4 5	Zone: 1 2 3 4 5
Average speed:	Average speed:
Max speed:	Max speed:
Inclination:	Inclination:
Food and water intake:	Food and water intake:
Ride report:	Ride report:
RPE: 1 – 10	RPE: 1 – 10

SUNDAY			
Energy	Sleep (hrs)	Sleep quality	Stress
Mood	Weather	Soreness	Weight
Injury/illness			

Ride 1	Ride 2
Resting heart rate:	Resting heart rate:
Route:	Route:
Distance:	Distance:
Time:	Time:
Zone: 1 2 3 4 5	Zone: 1 2 3 4 5
Average speed:	Average speed:
Max speed:	Max speed:
Inclination:	Inclination:
Food and water intake:	Food and water intake:
Ride report:	Ride report:
RPE: 1 – 10	RPE: 1 – 10

WEEKLY COMPETITION	
Race 1	Race 2
Time Goal:	Time Goal:
Resting heart rate:	Resting heart rate:
Weather:	Weather:
Route:	Route:
Distance:	Distance:
Time:	Time:
Zone: 1 2 3 4 5	Zone: 1 2 3 4 5
Average speed:	Average speed:
Inclination:	Inclination:
Notes:	Notes:

WEEKLY SUMMARY		
Weight	Distance	Time
Average speed	RPE: 1 – 10	
Notes:		

Week Beginning

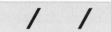

/ /

MONDAY			
Energy	Sleep (hrs)	Sleep quality	Stress
Mood	Weather	Soreness	Weight
Injury/illness			

Ride 1	Ride 2
Resting heart rate:	Resting heart rate:
Route:	Route:
Distance:	Distance:
Time:	Time:
Zone: 1 2 3 4 5	Zone: 1 2 3 4 5
Average speed:	Average speed:
Max speed:	Max speed:
Inclination:	Inclination:
Food and water intake:	Food and water intake:
Ride report:	Ride report:
RPE: 1 – 10	RPE: 1 – 10

TUESDAY			
Energy	Sleep (hrs)	Sleep quality	Stress
Mood	Weather	Soreness	Weight
Injury/illness			

Ride 1	Ride 2
Resting heart rate:	Resting heart rate:
Route:	Route:
Distance:	Distance:
Time:	Time:
Zone: 1 2 3 4 5	Zone: 1 2 3 4 5
Average speed:	Average speed:
Max speed:	Max speed:
Inclination:	Inclination:
Food and water intake:	Food and water intake:
Ride report:	Ride report:
RPE: 1 – 10	RPE: 1 – 10

Weekly Goals

WEDNESDAY			
Energy	Sleep (hrs)	Sleep quality	Stress
Mood	Weather	Soreness	Weight
Injury/illness			

Ride 1	Ride 2
Resting heart rate:	Resting heart rate:
Route:	Route:
Distance:	Distance:
Time:	Time:
Zone: 1 2 3 4 5	Zone: 1 2 3 4 5
Average speed:	Average speed:
Max speed:	Max speed:
Inclination:	Inclination:
Food and water intake:	Food and water intake:
Ride report:	Ride report:
RPE: 1 – 10	RPE: 1 – 10

THURSDAY			
Energy	Sleep (hrs)	Sleep quality	Stress
Mood	Weather	Soreness	Weight
Injury/illness			

Ride 1	Ride 2
Resting heart rate:	Resting heart rate:
Route:	Route:
Distance:	Distance:
Time:	Time:
Zone: 1 2 3 4 5	Zone: 1 2 3 4 5
Average speed:	Average speed:
Max speed:	Max speed:
Inclination:	Inclination:
Food and water intake:	Food and water intake:
Ride report:	Ride report:
RPE: 1 – 10	RPE: 1 – 10

FRIDAY			
Energy	Sleep (hrs)	Sleep quality	Stress
Mood	Weather	Soreness	Weight
Injury/illness			

Ride 1	Ride 2
Resting heart rate:	Resting heart rate:
Route:	Route:
Distance:	Distance:
Time:	Time:
Zone: 1 2 3 4 5	Zone: 1 2 3 4 5
Average speed:	Average speed:
Max speed:	Max speed:
Inclination:	Inclination:
Food and water intake:	Food and water intake:
Ride report:	Ride report:
RPE: 1 – 10	RPE: 1 – 10

SATURDAY			
Energy	Sleep (hrs)	Sleep quality	Stress
Mood	Weather	Soreness	Weight
Injury/illness			

Ride 1	Ride 2
Resting heart rate:	Resting heart rate:
Route:	Route:
Distance:	Distance:
Time:	Time:
Zone: 1 2 3 4 5	Zone: 1 2 3 4 5
Average speed:	Average speed:
Max speed:	Max speed:
Inclination:	Inclination:
Food and water intake:	Food and water intake:
Ride report:	Ride report:
RPE: 1 – 10	RPE: 1 – 10

SUNDAY			
Energy	Sleep (hrs)	Sleep quality	Stress
Mood	Weather	Soreness	Weight
Injury/illness			

Ride 1	Ride 2
Resting heart rate:	Resting heart rate:
Route:	Route:
Distance:	Distance:
Time:	Time:
Zone: 1 2 3 4 5	Zone: 1 2 3 4 5
Average speed:	Average speed:
Max speed:	Max speed:
Inclination:	Inclination:
Food and water intake:	Food and water intake:
Ride report:	Ride report:
RPE: 1 – 10	RPE: 1 – 10

WEEKLY COMPETITION	
Race 1	Race 2
Time Goal:	Time Goal:
Resting heart rate:	Resting heart rate:
Weather:	Weather:
Route:	Route:
Distance:	Distance:
Time:	Time:
Zone: 1 2 3 4 5	Zone: 1 2 3 4 5
Average speed:	Average speed:
Inclination:	Inclination:
Notes:	Notes:

WEEKLY SUMMARY			
Weight	Distance		Time
Average speed		RPE: 1 – 10	
Notes:			

Week Beginning

MONDAY			
Energy	Sleep (hrs)	Sleep quality	Stress
Mood	Weather	Soreness	Weight
Injury/illness			

Ride 1	Ride 2
Resting heart rate:	Resting heart rate:
Route:	Route:
Distance:	Distance:
Time:	Time:
Zone: 1 2 3 4 5	Zone: 1 2 3 4 5
Average speed:	Average speed:
Max speed:	Max speed:
Inclination:	Inclination:
Food and water intake:	Food and water intake:
Ride report:	Ride report:
RPE: 1 – 10	RPE: 1 – 10

TUESDAY			
Energy	Sleep (hrs)	Sleep quality	Stress
Mood	Weather	Soreness	Weight
Injury/illness			

Ride 1	Ride 2
Resting heart rate:	Resting heart rate:
Route:	Route:
Distance:	Distance:
Time:	Time:
Zone: 1 2 3 4 5	Zone: 1 2 3 4 5
Average speed:	Average speed:
Max speed:	Max speed:
Inclination:	Inclination:
Food and water intake:	Food and water intake:
Ride report:	Ride report:
RPE: 1 – 10	RPE: 1 – 10

Weekly Goals

WEDNESDAY			
Energy	Sleep (hrs)	Sleep quality	Stress
Mood	Weather	Soreness	Weight
Injury/illness			

Ride 1	Ride 2
Resting heart rate:	Resting heart rate:
Route:	Route:
Distance:	Distance:
Time:	Time:
Zone: 1 2 3 4 5	Zone: 1 2 3 4 5
Average speed:	Average speed:
Max speed:	Max speed:
Inclination:	Inclination:
Food and water intake:	Food and water intake:
Ride report:	Ride report:
RPE: 1 – 10	RPE: 1 – 10

THURSDAY			
Energy	Sleep (hrs)	Sleep quality	Stress
Mood	Weather	Soreness	Weight
Injury/illness			

Ride 1	Ride 2
Resting heart rate:	Resting heart rate:
Route:	Route:
Distance:	Distance:
Time:	Time:
Zone: 1 2 3 4 5	Zone: 1 2 3 4 5
Average speed:	Average speed:
Max speed:	Max speed:
Inclination:	Inclination:
Food and water intake:	Food and water intake:
Ride report:	Ride report:
RPE: 1 – 10	RPE: 1 – 10

FRIDAY			
Energy	Sleep (hrs)	Sleep quality	Stress
Mood	Weather	Soreness	Weight
Injury/illness			

Ride 1					Ride 2				
Resting heart rate:					Resting heart rate:				
Route:					Route:				
Distance:					Distance:				
Time:					Time:				
Zone: 1	2	3	4	5	Zone: 1	2	3	4	5
Average speed:					Average speed:				
Max speed:					Max speed:				
Inclination:					Inclination:				
Food and water intake:					Food and water intake:				
Ride report:					Ride report:				
RPE: 1 – 10					RPE: 1 – 10				

SATURDAY			
Energy	Sleep (hrs)	Sleep quality	Stress
Mood	Weather	Soreness	Weight
Injury/illness			

Ride 1					Ride 2				
Resting heart rate:					Resting heart rate:				
Route:					Route:				
Distance:					Distance:				
Time:					Time:				
Zone: 1	2	3	4	5	Zone: 1	2	3	4	5
Average speed:					Average speed:				
Max speed:					Max speed:				
Inclination:					Inclination:				
Food and water intake:					Food and water intake:				
Ride report:					Ride report:				
RPE: 1 – 10					RPE: 1 – 10				

SUNDAY			
Energy	Sleep (hrs)	Sleep quality	Stress
Mood	Weather	Soreness	Weight
Injury/illness			

Ride 1	Ride 2
Resting heart rate:	Resting heart rate:
Route:	Route:
Distance:	Distance:
Time:	Time:
Zone: 1 2 3 4 5	Zone: 1 2 3 4 5
Average speed:	Average speed:
Max speed:	Max speed:
Inclination:	Inclination:
Food and water intake:	Food and water intake:
Ride report:	Ride report:
RPE: 1 – 10	RPE: 1 – 10

WEEKLY COMPETITION	
Race 1	Race 2
Time Goal:	Time Goal:
Resting heart rate:	Resting heart rate:
Weather:	Weather:
Route:	Route:
Distance:	Distance:
Time:	Time:
Zone: 1 2 3 4 5	Zone: 1 2 3 4 5
Average speed:	Average speed:
Inclination:	Inclination:
Notes:	Notes:

WEEKLY SUMMARY			
Weight	Distance		Time
Average speed		RPE: 1 – 10	
Notes:			

Week Beginning

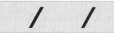

/ /

MONDAY

Energy		Sleep (hrs)		Sleep quality		Stress	
Mood		Weather		Soreness		Weight	
Injury/illness							

Ride 1	Ride 2
Resting heart rate:	Resting heart rate:
Route:	Route:
Distance:	Distance:
Time:	Time:
Zone: 1 2 3 4 5	Zone: 1 2 3 4 5
Average speed:	Average speed:
Max speed:	Max speed:
Inclination:	Inclination:
Food and water intake:	Food and water intake:
Ride report:	Ride report:
RPE: 1 – 10	RPE: 1 – 10

TUESDAY

Energy		Sleep (hrs)		Sleep quality		Stress	
Mood		Weather		Soreness		Weight	
Injury/illness							

Ride 1	Ride 2
Resting heart rate:	Resting heart rate:
Route:	Route:
Distance:	Distance:
Time:	Time:
Zone: 1 2 3 4 5	Zone: 1 2 3 4 5
Average speed:	Average speed:
Max speed:	Max speed:
Inclination:	Inclination:
Food and water intake:	Food and water intake:
Ride report:	Ride report:
RPE: 1 – 10	RPE: 1 – 10

Weekly Goals

WEDNESDAY			
Energy	Sleep (hrs)	Sleep quality	Stress
Mood	Weather	Soreness	Weight
Injury/illness			

Ride 1	Ride 2
Resting heart rate:	Resting heart rate:
Route:	Route:
Distance:	Distance:
Time:	Time:
Zone: 1 2 3 4 5	Zone: 1 2 3 4 5
Average speed:	Average speed:
Max speed:	Max speed:
Inclination:	Inclination:
Food and water intake:	Food and water intake:
Ride report:	Ride report:
RPE: 1 – 10	RPE: 1 – 10

THURSDAY			
Energy	Sleep (hrs)	Sleep quality	Stress
Mood	Weather	Soreness	Weight
Injury/illness			

Ride 1	Ride 2
Resting heart rate:	Resting heart rate:
Route:	Route:
Distance:	Distance:
Time:	Time:
Zone: 1 2 3 4 5	Zone: 1 2 3 4 5
Average speed:	Average speed:
Max speed:	Max speed:
Inclination:	Inclination:
Food and water intake:	Food and water intake:
Ride report:	Ride report:
RPE: 1 – 10	RPE: 1 – 10

FRIDAY			
Energy	Sleep (hrs)	Sleep quality	Stress
Mood	Weather	Soreness	Weight
Injury/illness			

Ride 1	Ride 2
Resting heart rate:	Resting heart rate:
Route:	Route:
Distance:	Distance:
Time:	Time:
Zone: 1 2 3 4 5	Zone: 1 2 3 4 5
Average speed:	Average speed:
Max speed:	Max speed:
Inclination:	Inclination:
Food and water intake:	Food and water intake:
Ride report:	Ride report:
RPE: 1 – 10	RPE: 1 – 10

SATURDAY			
Energy	Sleep (hrs)	Sleep quality	Stress
Mood	Weather	Soreness	Weight
Injury/illness			

Ride 1	Ride 2
Resting heart rate:	Resting heart rate:
Route:	Route:
Distance:	Distance:
Time:	Time:
Zone: 1 2 3 4 5	Zone: 1 2 3 4 5
Average speed:	Average speed:
Max speed:	Max speed:
Inclination:	Inclination:
Food and water intake:	Food and water intake:
Ride report:	Ride report:
RPE: 1 – 10	RPE: 1 – 10

SUNDAY			
Energy	Sleep (hrs)	Sleep quality	Stress
Mood	Weather	Soreness	Weight
Injury/illness			

Ride 1	Ride 2
Resting heart rate:	Resting heart rate:
Route:	Route:
Distance:	Distance:
Time:	Time:
Zone: 1 2 3 4 5	Zone: 1 2 3 4 5
Average speed:	Average speed:
Max speed:	Max speed:
Inclination:	Inclination:
Food and water intake:	Food and water intake:
Ride report:	Ride report:
RPE: 1 – 10	RPE: 1 – 10

WEEKLY COMPETITION	
Race 1	Race 2
Time Goal:	Time Goal:
Resting heart rate:	Resting heart rate:
Weather:	Weather:
Route:	Route:
Distance:	Distance:
Time:	Time:
Zone: 1 2 3 4 5	Zone: 1 2 3 4 5
Average speed:	Average speed:
Inclination:	Inclination:
Notes:	Notes:

WEEKLY SUMMARY		
Weight	Distance	Time
Average speed	RPE: 1 – 10	
Notes:		

Week Beginning

/ /

MONDAY			
Energy	Sleep (hrs)	Sleep quality	Stress
Mood	Weather	Soreness	Weight
Injury/illness			

Ride 1	Ride 2
Resting heart rate:	Resting heart rate:
Route:	Route:
Distance:	Distance:
Time:	Time:
Zone: 1 2 3 4 5	Zone: 1 2 3 4 5
Average speed:	Average speed:
Max speed:	Max speed:
Inclination:	Inclination:
Food and water intake:	Food and water intake:
Ride report:	Ride report:
RPE: 1 – 10	RPE: 1 – 10

TUESDAY			
Energy	Sleep (hrs)	Sleep quality	Stress
Mood	Weather	Soreness	Weight
Injury/illness			

Ride 1	Ride 2
Resting heart rate:	Resting heart rate:
Route:	Route:
Distance:	Distance:
Time:	Time:
Zone: 1 2 3 4 5	Zone: 1 2 3 4 5
Average speed:	Average speed:
Max speed:	Max speed:
Inclination:	Inclination:
Food and water intake:	Food and water intake:
Ride report:	Ride report:
RPE: 1 – 10	RPE: 1 – 10

Weekly Goals

WEDNESDAY			
Energy	Sleep (hrs)	Sleep quality	Stress
Mood	Weather	Soreness	Weight
Injury/illness			

Ride 1	Ride 2
Resting heart rate:	Resting heart rate:
Route:	Route:
Distance:	Distance:
Time:	Time:
Zone: 1 2 3 4 5	Zone: 1 2 3 4 5
Average speed:	Average speed:
Max speed:	Max speed:
Inclination:	Inclination:
Food and water intake:	Food and water intake:
Ride report:	Ride report:
RPE: 1 – 10	RPE: 1 – 10

THURSDAY			
Energy	Sleep (hrs)	Sleep quality	Stress
Mood	Weather	Soreness	Weight
Injury/illness			

Ride 1	Ride 2
Resting heart rate:	Resting heart rate:
Route:	Route:
Distance:	Distance:
Time:	Time:
Zone: 1 2 3 4 5	Zone: 1 2 3 4 5
Average speed:	Average speed:
Max speed:	Max speed:
Inclination:	Inclination:
Food and water intake:	Food and water intake:
Ride report:	Ride report:
RPE: 1 – 10	RPE: 1 – 10

FRIDAY			
Energy	Sleep (hrs)	Sleep quality	Stress
Mood	Weather	Soreness	Weight
Injury/illness			

Ride 1	Ride 2
Resting heart rate:	Resting heart rate:
Route:	Route:
Distance:	Distance:
Time:	Time:
Zone: 1 2 3 4 5	Zone: 1 2 3 4 5
Average speed:	Average speed:
Max speed:	Max speed:
Inclination:	Inclination:
Food and water intake:	Food and water intake:
Ride report:	Ride report:
RPE: 1 – 10	RPE: 1 – 10

SATURDAY			
Energy	Sleep (hrs)	Sleep quality	Stress
Mood	Weather	Soreness	Weight
Injury/illness			

Ride 1	Ride 2
Resting heart rate:	Resting heart rate:
Route:	Route:
Distance:	Distance:
Time:	Time:
Zone: 1 2 3 4 5	Zone: 1 2 3 4 5
Average speed:	Average speed:
Max speed:	Max speed:
Inclination:	Inclination:
Food and water intake:	Food and water intake:
Ride report:	Ride report:
RPE: 1 – 10	RPE: 1 – 10

SUNDAY			
Energy	Sleep (hrs)	Sleep quality	Stress
Mood	Weather	Soreness	Weight
Injury/illness			

Ride 1	Ride 2
Resting heart rate:	Resting heart rate:
Route:	Route:
Distance:	Distance:
Time:	Time:
Zone: 1 2 3 4 5	Zone: 1 2 3 4 5
Average speed:	Average speed:
Max speed:	Max speed:
Inclination:	Inclination:
Food and water intake:	Food and water intake:
Ride report:	Ride report:
RPE: 1 – 10	RPE: 1 – 10

WEEKLY COMPETITION	
Race 1	Race 2
Time Goal:	Time Goal:
Resting heart rate:	Resting heart rate:
Weather:	Weather:
Route:	Route:
Distance:	Distance:
Time:	Time:
Zone: 1 2 3 4 5	Zone: 1 2 3 4 5
Average speed:	Average speed:
Inclination:	Inclination:
Notes:	Notes:

WEEKLY SUMMARY		
Weight	Distance	Time
Average speed	RPE: 1 – 10	
Notes:		

Week Beginning

 / /

MONDAY

Energy		Sleep (hrs)		Sleep quality		Stress	
Mood		Weather		Soreness		Weight	

Injury/illness

Ride 1	Ride 2
Resting heart rate:	Resting heart rate:
Route:	Route:
Distance:	Distance:
Time:	Time:
Zone: 1 2 3 4 5	Zone: 1 2 3 4 5
Average speed:	Average speed:
Max speed:	Max speed:
Inclination:	Inclination:
Food and water intake:	Food and water intake:
Ride report:	Ride report:
RPE: 1 – 10	RPE: 1 – 10

TUESDAY

Energy		Sleep (hrs)		Sleep quality		Stress	
Mood		Weather		Soreness		Weight	

Injury/illness

Ride 1	Ride 2
Resting heart rate:	Resting heart rate:
Route:	Route:
Distance:	Distance:
Time:	Time:
Zone: 1 2 3 4 5	Zone: 1 2 3 4 5
Average speed:	Average speed:
Max speed:	Max speed:
Inclination:	Inclination:
Food and water intake:	Food and water intake:
Ride report:	Ride report:
RPE: 1 – 10	RPE: 1 – 10

Weekly Goals

WEDNESDAY			
Energy	Sleep (hrs)	Sleep quality	Stress
Mood	Weather	Soreness	Weight
Injury/illness			

Ride 1	Ride 2
Resting heart rate:	Resting heart rate:
Route:	Route:
Distance:	Distance:
Time:	Time:
Zone: 1 2 3 4 5	Zone: 1 2 3 4 5
Average speed:	Average speed:
Max speed:	Max speed:
Inclination:	Inclination:
Food and water intake:	Food and water intake:
Ride report:	Ride report:
RPE: 1 – 10	RPE: 1 – 10

THURSDAY			
Energy	Sleep (hrs)	Sleep quality	Stress
Mood	Weather	Soreness	Weight
Injury/illness			

Ride 1	Ride 2
Resting heart rate:	Resting heart rate:
Route:	Route:
Distance:	Distance:
Time:	Time:
Zone: 1 2 3 4 5	Zone: 1 2 3 4 5
Average speed:	Average speed:
Max speed:	Max speed:
Inclination:	Inclination:
Food and water intake:	Food and water intake:
Ride report:	Ride report:
RPE: 1 – 10	RPE: 1 – 10

FRIDAY			
Energy	Sleep (hrs)	Sleep quality	Stress
Mood	Weather	Soreness	Weight
Injury/illness			

Ride 1	Ride 2
Resting heart rate:	Resting heart rate:
Route:	Route:
Distance:	Distance:
Time:	Time:
Zone: 1 2 3 4 5	Zone: 1 2 3 4 5
Average speed:	Average speed:
Max speed:	Max speed:
Inclination:	Inclination:
Food and water intake:	Food and water intake:
Ride report:	Ride report:
RPE: 1 – 10	RPE: 1 – 10

SATURDAY			
Energy	Sleep (hrs)	Sleep quality	Stress
Mood	Weather	Soreness	Weight
Injury/illness			

Ride 1	Ride 2
Resting heart rate:	Resting heart rate:
Route:	Route:
Distance:	Distance:
Time:	Time:
Zone: 1 2 3 4 5	Zone: 1 2 3 4 5
Average speed:	Average speed:
Max speed:	Max speed:
Inclination:	Inclination:
Food and water intake:	Food and water intake:
Ride report:	Ride report:
RPE: 1 – 10	RPE: 1 – 10

SUNDAY			
Energy	Sleep (hrs)	Sleep quality	Stress
Mood	Weather	Soreness	Weight
Injury/illness			

Ride 1	Ride 2
Resting heart rate:	Resting heart rate:
Route:	Route:
Distance:	Distance:
Time:	Time:
Zone: 1 2 3 4 5	Zone: 1 2 3 4 5
Average speed:	Average speed:
Max speed:	Max speed:
Inclination:	Inclination:
Food and water intake:	Food and water intake:
Ride report:	Ride report:
RPE: 1 – 10	RPE: 1 – 10

WEEKLY COMPETITION	
Race 1	Race 2
Time Goal:	Time Goal:
Resting heart rate:	Resting heart rate:
Weather:	Weather:
Route:	Route:
Distance:	Distance:
Time:	Time:
Zone: 1 2 3 4 5	Zone: 1 2 3 4 5
Average speed:	Average speed:
Inclination:	Inclination:
Notes:	Notes:

WEEKLY SUMMARY			
Weight		Distance	Time
Average speed		RPE: 1 – 10	
Notes:			

Week Beginning

MONDAY			
Energy	Sleep (hrs)	Sleep quality	Stress
Mood	Weather	Soreness	Weight
Injury/illness			

Ride 1	Ride 2
Resting heart rate:	Resting heart rate:
Route:	Route:
Distance:	Distance:
Time:	Time:
Zone: 1 2 3 4 5	Zone: 1 2 3 4 5
Average speed:	Average speed:
Max speed:	Max speed:
Inclination:	Inclination:
Food and water intake:	Food and water intake:
Ride report:	Ride report:
RPE: 1 – 10	RPE: 1 – 10

TUESDAY			
Energy	Sleep (hrs)	Sleep quality	Stress
Mood	Weather	Soreness	Weight
Injury/illness			

Ride 1	Ride 2
Resting heart rate:	Resting heart rate:
Route:	Route:
Distance:	Distance:
Time:	Time:
Zone: 1 2 3 4 5	Zone: 1 2 3 4 5
Average speed:	Average speed:
Max speed:	Max speed:
Inclination:	Inclination:
Food and water intake:	Food and water intake:
Ride report:	Ride report:
RPE: 1 – 10	RPE: 1 – 10

Weekly Goals

WEDNESDAY			
Energy	Sleep (hrs)	Sleep quality	Stress
Mood	Weather	Soreness	Weight
Injury/illness			

Ride 1	Ride 2
Resting heart rate:	Resting heart rate:
Route:	Route:
Distance:	Distance:
Time:	Time:
Zone: 1 2 3 4 5	Zone: 1 2 3 4 5
Average speed:	Average speed:
Max speed:	Max speed:
Inclination:	Inclination:
Food and water intake:	Food and water intake:
Ride report:	Ride report:
RPE: 1 – 10	RPE: 1 – 10

THURSDAY			
Energy	Sleep (hrs)	Sleep quality	Stress
Mood	Weather	Soreness	Weight
Injury/illness			

Ride 1	Ride 2
Resting heart rate:	Resting heart rate:
Route:	Route:
Distance:	Distance:
Time:	Time:
Zone: 1 2 3 4 5	Zone: 1 2 3 4 5
Average speed:	Average speed:
Max speed:	Max speed:
Inclination:	Inclination:
Food and water intake:	Food and water intake:
Ride report:	Ride report:
RPE: 1 – 10	RPE: 1 – 10

FRIDAY

Energy		Sleep (hrs)		Sleep quality		Stress	
Mood		Weather		Soreness		Weight	
Injury/illness							

Ride 1	Ride 2
Resting heart rate:	Resting heart rate:
Route:	Route:
Distance:	Distance:
Time:	Time:
Zone: 1 2 3 4 5	Zone: 1 2 3 4 5
Average speed:	Average speed:
Max speed:	Max speed:
Inclination:	Inclination:
Food and water intake:	Food and water intake:
Ride report:	Ride report:
RPE: 1 – 10	RPE: 1 – 10

SATURDAY

Energy		Sleep (hrs)		Sleep quality		Stress	
Mood		Weather		Soreness		Weight	
Injury/illness							

Ride 1	Ride 2
Resting heart rate:	Resting heart rate:
Route:	Route:
Distance:	Distance:
Time:	Time:
Zone: 1 2 3 4 5	Zone: 1 2 3 4 5
Average speed:	Average speed:
Max speed:	Max speed:
Inclination:	Inclination:
Food and water intake:	Food and water intake:
Ride report:	Ride report:
RPE: 1 – 10	RPE: 1 – 10

SUNDAY			
Energy	Sleep (hrs)	Sleep quality	Stress
Mood	Weather	Soreness	Weight
Injury/illness			

Ride 1	Ride 2
Resting heart rate:	Resting heart rate:
Route:	Route:
Distance:	Distance:
Time:	Time:
Zone: 1 2 3 4 5	Zone: 1 2 3 4 5
Average speed:	Average speed:
Max speed:	Max speed:
Inclination:	Inclination:
Food and water intake:	Food and water intake:
Ride report:	Ride report:
RPE: 1 – 10	RPE: 1 – 10

WEEKLY COMPETITION	
Race 1	Race 2
Time Goal:	Time Goal:
Resting heart rate:	Resting heart rate:
Weather:	Weather:
Route:	Route:
Distance:	Distance:
Time:	Time:
Zone: 1 2 3 4 5	Zone: 1 2 3 4 5
Average speed:	Average speed:
Inclination:	Inclination:
Notes:	Notes:

WEEKLY SUMMARY		
Weight	Distance	Time
Average speed	RPE: 1 – 10	
Notes:		

Week Beginning

/ /

MONDAY			
Energy	Sleep (hrs)	Sleep quality	Stress
Mood	Weather	Soreness	Weight
Injury/illness			

Ride 1	Ride 2
Resting heart rate:	Resting heart rate:
Route:	Route:
Distance:	Distance:
Time:	Time:
Zone: 1 2 3 4 5	Zone: 1 2 3 4 5
Average speed:	Average speed:
Max speed:	Max speed:
Inclination:	Inclination:
Food and water intake:	Food and water intake:
Ride report:	Ride report:
RPE: 1 – 10	RPE: 1 – 10

TUESDAY			
Energy	Sleep (hrs)	Sleep quality	Stress
Mood	Weather	Soreness	Weight
Injury/illness			

Ride 1	Ride 2
Resting heart rate:	Resting heart rate:
Route:	Route:
Distance:	Distance:
Time:	Time:
Zone: 1 2 3 4 5	Zone: 1 2 3 4 5
Average speed:	Average speed:
Max speed:	Max speed:
Inclination:	Inclination:
Food and water intake:	Food and water intake:
Ride report:	Ride report:
RPE: 1 – 10	RPE: 1 – 10

Weekly Goals

WEDNESDAY			
Energy	Sleep (hrs)	Sleep quality	Stress
Mood	Weather	Soreness	Weight
Injury/illness			

Ride 1	Ride 2
Resting heart rate:	Resting heart rate:
Route:	Route:
Distance:	Distance:
Time:	Time:
Zone: 1 2 3 4 5	Zone: 1 2 3 4 5
Average speed:	Average speed:
Max speed:	Max speed:
Inclination:	Inclination:
Food and water intake:	Food and water intake:
Ride report:	Ride report:
RPE: 1 – 10	RPE: 1 – 10

THURSDAY			
Energy	Sleep (hrs)	Sleep quality	Stress
Mood	Weather	Soreness	Weight
Injury/illness			

Ride 1	Ride 2
Resting heart rate:	Resting heart rate:
Route:	Route:
Distance:	Distance:
Time:	Time:
Zone: 1 2 3 4 5	Zone: 1 2 3 4 5
Average speed:	Average speed:
Max speed:	Max speed:
Inclination:	Inclination:
Food and water intake:	Food and water intake:
Ride report:	Ride report:
RPE: 1 – 10	RPE: 1 – 10

FRIDAY			
Energy	Sleep (hrs)	Sleep quality	Stress
Mood	Weather	Soreness	Weight
Injury/illness			

Ride 1		Ride 2	
Resting heart rate:		Resting heart rate:	
Route:		Route:	
Distance:		Distance:	
Time:		Time:	
Zone: 1 2 3 4 5		Zone: 1 2 3 4 5	
Average speed:		Average speed:	
Max speed:		Max speed:	
Inclination:		Inclination:	
Food and water intake:		Food and water intake:	
Ride report:		Ride report:	
RPE: 1 – 10		RPE: 1 – 10	

SATURDAY			
Energy	Sleep (hrs)	Sleep quality	Stress
Mood	Weather	Soreness	Weight
Injury/illness			

Ride 1		Ride 2	
Resting heart rate:		Resting heart rate:	
Route:		Route:	
Distance:		Distance:	
Time:		Time:	
Zone: 1 2 3 4 5		Zone: 1 2 3 4 5	
Average speed:		Average speed:	
Max speed:		Max speed:	
Inclination:		Inclination:	
Food and water intake:		Food and water intake:	
Ride report:		Ride report:	
RPE: 1 – 10		RPE: 1 – 10	

SUNDAY			
Energy	Sleep (hrs)	Sleep quality	Stress
Mood	Weather	Soreness	Weight
Injury/illness			

Ride 1	Ride 2
Resting heart rate:	Resting heart rate:
Route:	Route:
Distance:	Distance:
Time:	Time:
Zone: 1 2 3 4 5	Zone: 1 2 3 4 5
Average speed:	Average speed:
Max speed:	Max speed:
Inclination:	Inclination:
Food and water intake:	Food and water intake:
Ride report:	Ride report:
RPE: 1 – 10	RPE: 1 – 10

WEEKLY COMPETITION	
Race 1	Race 2
Time Goal:	Time Goal:
Resting heart rate:	Resting heart rate:
Weather:	Weather:
Route:	Route:
Distance:	Distance:
Time:	Time:
Zone: 1 2 3 4 5	Zone: 1 2 3 4 5
Average speed:	Average speed:
Inclination:	Inclination:
Notes:	Notes:

WEEKLY SUMMARY		
Weight	Distance	Time
Average speed	RPE: 1 – 10	
Notes:		

Week Beginning

/ /

MONDAY			
Energy	Sleep (hrs)	Sleep quality	Stress
Mood	Weather	Soreness	Weight
Injury/illness			

Ride 1	Ride 2
Resting heart rate:	Resting heart rate:
Route:	Route:
Distance:	Distance:
Time:	Time:
Zone: 1 2 3 4 5	Zone: 1 2 3 4 5
Average speed:	Average speed:
Max speed:	Max speed:
Inclination:	Inclination:
Food and water intake:	Food and water intake:
Ride report:	Ride report:
RPE: 1 – 10	RPE: 1 – 10

TUESDAY			
Energy	Sleep (hrs)	Sleep quality	Stress
Mood	Weather	Soreness	Weight
Injury/illness			

Ride 1	Ride 2
Resting heart rate:	Resting heart rate:
Route:	Route:
Distance:	Distance:
Time:	Time:
Zone: 1 2 3 4 5	Zone: 1 2 3 4 5
Average speed:	Average speed:
Max speed:	Max speed:
Inclination:	Inclination:
Food and water intake:	Food and water intake:
Ride report:	Ride report:
RPE: 1 – 10	RPE: 1 – 10

Weekly Goals

WEDNESDAY			
Energy	Sleep (hrs)	Sleep quality	Stress
Mood	Weather	Soreness	Weight
Injury/illness			

Ride 1	Ride 2
Resting heart rate:	Resting heart rate:
Route:	Route:
Distance:	Distance:
Time:	Time:
Zone: 1 2 3 4 5	Zone: 1 2 3 4 5
Average speed:	Average speed:
Max speed:	Max speed:
Inclination:	Inclination:
Food and water intake:	Food and water intake:
Ride report:	Ride report:
RPE: 1 – 10	RPE: 1 – 10

THURSDAY			
Energy	Sleep (hrs)	Sleep quality	Stress
Mood	Weather	Soreness	Weight
Injury/illness			

Ride 1	Ride 2
Resting heart rate:	Resting heart rate:
Route:	Route:
Distance:	Distance:
Time:	Time:
Zone: 1 2 3 4 5	Zone: 1 2 3 4 5
Average speed:	Average speed:
Max speed:	Max speed:
Inclination:	Inclination:
Food and water intake:	Food and water intake:
Ride report:	Ride report:
RPE: 1 – 10	RPE: 1 – 10

Week Beginning / / Continued

FRIDAY			
Energy	Sleep (hrs)	Sleep quality	Stress
Mood	Weather	Soreness	Weight
Injury/illness			

Ride 1	Ride 2
Resting heart rate:	Resting heart rate:
Route:	Route:
Distance:	Distance:
Time:	Time:
Zone: 1 2 3 4 5	Zone: 1 2 3 4 5
Average speed:	Average speed:
Max speed:	Max speed:
Inclination:	Inclination:
Food and water intake:	Food and water intake:
Ride report:	Ride report:
RPE: 1 – 10	RPE: 1 – 10

SATURDAY			
Energy	Sleep (hrs)	Sleep quality	Stress
Mood	Weather	Soreness	Weight
Injury/illness			

Ride 1	Ride 2
Resting heart rate:	Resting heart rate:
Route:	Route:
Distance:	Distance:
Time:	Time:
Zone: 1 2 3 4 5	Zone: 1 2 3 4 5
Average speed:	Average speed:
Max speed:	Max speed:
Inclination:	Inclination:
Food and water intake:	Food and water intake:
Ride report:	Ride report:
RPE: 1 – 10	RPE: 1 – 10

SUNDAY				
Energy	Sleep (hrs)		Sleep quality	Stress
Mood	Weather		Soreness	Weight
Injury/illness				

Ride 1	Ride 2
Resting heart rate:	Resting heart rate:
Route:	Route:
Distance:	Distance:
Time:	Time:
Zone: 1 2 3 4 5	Zone: 1 2 3 4 5
Average speed:	Average speed:
Max speed:	Max speed:
Inclination:	Inclination:
Food and water intake:	Food and water intake:
Ride report:	Ride report:
RPE: 1 – 10	RPE: 1 – 10

WEEKLY COMPETITION	
Race 1	Race 2
Time Goal:	Time Goal:
Resting heart rate:	Resting heart rate:
Weather:	Weather:
Route:	Route:
Distance:	Distance:
Time:	Time:
Zone: 1 2 3 4 5	Zone: 1 2 3 4 5
Average speed:	Average speed:
Inclination:	Inclination:
Notes:	Notes:

WEEKLY SUMMARY			
Weight	Distance		Time
Average speed		RPE: 1 – 10	
Notes:			

Monthly Summary

MONTH **1**   DATE [/ /]

Targets Versus Results

Last Month's Target		This Month's Result
	Average weight	
	Average resting heart rate	
	Average distance	
	Total distance	
	Average time	
	Total time	
	Average zone	
	Average speed	
	Maximum speed	
	Average inclination	
	Average RPE	

Fitness Test

	Last Month	Target	Actual	Next Mth's Target
Working heart rate: after 4 minutes				
after 8 minutes				
after 12 minutes				
Recovery heart rate: at course completion				
1 minute after completion				
2 minutes after completion				
3 minutes after completion				
Time to cycle 3 miles/5km				
Completion time				

Total your weekly results and divide by the number of weeks to get your average.

Average monthly mood — 1–5 [ ]

Average monthly appetite — 1–5 [ ]

Average monthly energy level — 1–5 [ ]

Average monthly stress level — 1–5 [ ]

Average weekly hours of sleep [ ]

Average monthly sleep quality — 1–5 [ ]

Average monthly soreness level — 1–5 [ ]

Next Month's Targets

	Next Month's Target
Weight	
Resting heart rate	
Distance	
Time	
Zone	
Average speed	
Maximum speed	
Inclination	
RPE	

Injuries/Illnesses

Monthly Notes

Monthly Summary

MONTH **2**   DATE [/ /]

Targets Versus Results

Last Month's Target		This Month's Result
	Average weight	
	Average resting heart rate	
	Average distance	
	Total distance	
	Average time	
	Total time	
	Average zone	
	Average speed	
	Maximum speed	
	Average inclination	
	Average RPE	

Fitness Test

	Last Month	Target	Actual	Next Mth's Target
Working heart rate: after 4 minutes				
after 8 minutes				
after 12 minutes				
Recovery heart rate: at course completion				
1 minute after completion				
2 minutes after completion				
3 minutes after completion				
Time to cycle 3 miles/5km				
Completion time				

Total your weekly results and divide by the number of weeks to get your average.

Average monthly mood [1–5]

Average monthly appetite [1–5]

Average monthly energy level [1–5]

Average monthly stress level [1–5]

Average weekly hours of sleep [ ]

Average monthly sleep quality [1–5]

Average monthly soreness level [1–5]

Next Month's Targets

	Next Month's Target
Weight	
Resting heart rate	
Distance	
Time	
Zone	
Average speed	
Maximum speed	
Inclination	
RPE	

Injuries/Illnesses

Monthly Notes

Monthly Summary

MONTH **3**   DATE [/ /]

Targets Versus Results

Last Month's Target		This Month's Result
	Average weight	
	Average resting heart rate	
	Average distance	
	Total distance	
	Average time	
	Total time	
	Average zone	
	Average speed	
	Maximum speed	
	Average inclination	
	Average RPE	

Fitness Test

	Last Month	Target	Actual	Next Mth's Target
Working heart rate: after 4 minutes				
after 8 minutes				
after 12 minutes				
Recovery heart rate: at course completion				
1 minute after completion				
2 minutes after completion				
3 minutes after completion				
Time to cycle 3 miles/5km				
Completion time				

Total your weekly results and divide by the number of weeks to get your average.

Average monthly mood   1–5 [ ]

Average monthly appetite   1–5 [ ]

Average monthly energy level   1–5 [ ]

Average monthly stress level   1–5 [ ]

Average weekly hours of sleep   [ ]

Average monthly sleep quality   1–5 [ ]

Average monthly soreness level   1–5 [ ]

Next Month's Targets

	Next Month's Target
Weight	
Resting heart rate	
Distance	
Time	
Zone	
Average speed	
Maximum speed	
Inclination	
RPE	

Injuries/Illnesses

Monthly Notes

Monthly Summary

MONTH **4** DATE / /

Targets Versus Results

Last Month's Target		This Month's Result
	Average weight	
	Average resting heart rate	
	Average distance	
	Total distance	
	Average time	
	Total time	
	Average zone	
	Average speed	
	Maximum speed	
	Average inclination	
	Average RPE	

Fitness Test

		Last Month	Target	Actual	Next Mth's Target
Working heart rate:	after 4 minutes				
	after 8 minutes				
	after 12 minutes				
Recovery heart rate:	at course completion				
	1 minute after completion				
	2 minutes after completion				
	3 minutes after completion				
Time to cycle 3 miles/5km					
Completion time					

Total your weekly results and divide by the number of weeks to get your average.

Average monthly mood [1–5]

Average monthly appetite [1–5]

Average monthly energy level [1–5]

Average monthly stress level [1–5]

Average weekly hours of sleep

Average monthly sleep quality [1–5]

Average monthly soreness level [1–5]

Next Month's Targets

	Next Month's Target
Weight	
Resting heart rate	
Distance	
Time	
Zone	
Average speed	
Maximum speed	
Inclination	
RPE	

Injuries/Illnesses

Monthly Notes

Monthly Summary

MONTH **5**   DATE [/ /]

Targets Versus Results

Last Month's Target		This Month's Result
	Average weight	
	Average resting heart rate	
	Average distance	
	Total distance	
	Average time	
	Total time	
	Average zone	
	Average speed	
	Maximum speed	
	Average inclination	
	Average RPE	

Fitness Test

	Last Month	Target	Actual	Next Mth's Target
Working heart rate: after 4 minutes				
after 8 minutes				
after 12 minutes				
Recovery heart rate: at course completion				
1 minute after completion				
2 minutes after completion				
3 minutes after completion				
Time to cycle 3 miles/5km				
Completion time				

Total your weekly results and divide by the number of weeks to get your average.

Average monthly mood [1–5]

Average monthly appetite [1–5]

Average monthly energy level [1–5]

Average monthly stress level [1–5]

Average weekly hours of sleep [ ]

Average monthly sleep quality [1–5]

Average monthly soreness level [1–5]

Next Month's Targets

	Next Month's Target
Weight	
Resting heart rate	
Distance	
Time	
Zone	
Average speed	
Maximum speed	
Inclination	
RPE	

Injuries/Illnesses

Monthly Notes

Monthly Summary

MONTH **6**   DATE [/ /]

Targets Versus Results

Last Month's Target		This Month's Result
	Average weight	
	Average resting heart rate	
	Average distance	
	Total distance	
	Average time	
	Total time	
	Average zone	
	Average speed	
	Maximum speed	
	Average inclination	
	Average RPE	

Fitness Test

	Last Month	Target	Actual	Next Mth's Target
Working heart rate: after 4 minutes				
after 8 minutes				
after 12 minutes				
Recovery heart rate: at course completion				
1 minute after completion				
2 minutes after completion				
3 minutes after completion				
Time to cycle 3 miles/5km				
Completion time				

Total your weekly results and divide by the number of weeks to get your average.

Average monthly mood — 1–5 [ ]

Average monthly appetite — 1–5 [ ]

Average monthly energy level — 1–5 [ ]

Average monthly stress level — 1–5 [ ]

Average weekly hours of sleep [ ]

Average monthly sleep quality — 1–5 [ ]

Average monthly soreness level — 1–5 [ ]

Next Month's Targets

	Next Month's Target
Weight	
Resting heart rate	
Distance	
Time	
Zone	
Average speed	
Maximum speed	
Inclination	
RPE	

Injuries/Illnesses

Monthly Notes

Monthly Summary

MONTH **7**   DATE [/ /]

Targets Versus Results

Last Month's Target		This Month's Result
	Average weight	
	Average resting heart rate	
	Average distance	
	Total distance	
	Average time	
	Total time	
	Average zone	
	Average speed	
	Maximum speed	
	Average inclination	
	Average RPE	

Fitness Test

	Last Month	Target	Actual	Next Mth's Target
Working heart rate: after 4 minutes				
after 8 minutes				
after 12 minutes				
Recovery heart rate: at course completion				
1 minute after completion				
2 minutes after completion				
3 minutes after completion				
Time to cycle 3 miles/5km				
Completion time				

Total your weekly results and divide by the number of weeks to get your average.

Average monthly mood   1–5 [ ]

Average monthly appetite   1–5 [ ]

Average monthly energy level   1–5 [ ]

Average monthly stress level   1–5 [ ]

Average weekly hours of sleep   [ ]

Average monthly sleep quality   1–5 [ ]

Average monthly soreness level   1–5 [ ]

Next Month's Targets

	Next Month's Target
Weight	
Resting heart rate	
Distance	
Time	
Zone	
Average speed	
Maximum speed	
Inclination	
RPE	

Injuries/Illnesses

Monthly Notes

Monthly Summary

MONTH **8** DATE [/ /]

Targets Versus Results

Last Month's Target		This Month's Result
	Average weight	
	Average resting heart rate	
	Average distance	
	Total distance	
	Average time	
	Total time	
	Average zone	
	Average speed	
	Maximum speed	
	Average inclination	
	Average RPE	

Fitness Test

	Last Month	Target	Actual	Next Mth's Target
Working heart rate: after 4 minutes				
after 8 minutes				
after 12 minutes				
Recovery heart rate: at course completion				
1 minute after completion				
2 minutes after completion				
3 minutes after completion				
Time to cycle 3 miles/5km				
Completion time				

Total your weekly results and divide by the number of weeks to get your average.

Average monthly mood — 1–5 [ ]

Average monthly appetite — 1–5 [ ]

Average monthly energy level — 1–5 [ ]

Average monthly stress level — 1–5 [ ]

Average weekly hours of sleep [ ]

Average monthly sleep quality — 1–5 [ ]

Average monthly soreness level — 1–5 [ ]

Next Month's Targets

	Next Month's Target
Weight	
Resting heart rate	
Distance	
Time	
Zone	
Average speed	
Maximum speed	
Inclination	
RPE	

Injuries/Illnesses

Monthly Notes

Monthly Summary

MONTH **9** DATE [/ /]

Targets Versus Results

Last Month's Target		This Month's Result
	Average weight	
	Average resting heart rate	
	Average distance	
	Total distance	
	Average time	
	Total time	
	Average zone	
	Average speed	
	Maximum speed	
	Average inclination	
	Average RPE	

Fitness Test

		Last Month	Target	Actual	Next Mth's Target
Working heart rate:	after 4 minutes				
	after 8 minutes				
	after 12 minutes				
Recovery heart rate:	at course completion				
	1 minute after completion				
	2 minutes after completion				
	3 minutes after completion				
Time to cycle 3 miles/5km					
Completion time					

Total your weekly results and divide by the number of weeks to get your average.

Average monthly mood   1–5 [ ]

Average monthly appetite   1–5 [ ]

Average monthly energy level   1–5 [ ]

Average monthly stress level   1–5 [ ]

Average weekly hours of sleep [ ]

Average monthly sleep quality   1–5 [ ]

Average monthly soreness level   1–5 [ ]

Next Month's Targets

	Next Month's Target
Weight	
Resting heart rate	
Distance	
Time	
Zone	
Average speed	
Maximum speed	
Inclination	
RPE	

Injuries/Illnesses

Monthly Notes

Monthly Summary

MONTH **10** DATE [/ /]

Targets Versus Results		
Last Month's Target		**This Month's Result**
	Average weight	
	Average resting heart rate	
	Average distance	
	Total distance	
	Average time	
	Total time	
	Average zone	
	Average speed	
	Maximum speed	
	Average inclination	
	Average RPE	

Fitness Test				
	Last Month	Target	Actual	Next Mth's Target
Working heart rate: after 4 minutes				
after 8 minutes				
after 12 minutes				
Recovery heart rate: at course completion				
1 minute after completion				
2 minutes after completion				
3 minutes after completion				
Time to cycle 3 miles/5km				
Completion time				

Total your weekly results and divide by the number of weeks to get your average.

Average monthly mood [1–5]

Average monthly appetite [1–5]

Average monthly energy level [1–5]

Average monthly stress level [1–5]

Average weekly hours of sleep [ ]

Average monthly sleep quality [1–5]

Average monthly soreness level [1–5]

Next Month's Targets

	Next Month's Target
Weight	
Resting heart rate	
Distance	
Time	
Zone	
Average speed	
Maximum speed	
Inclination	
RPE	

Injuries/Illnesses

Monthly Notes

Monthly Summary

MONTH **11** DATE [/ /]

Targets Versus Results

Last Month's Target		This Month's Result
	Average weight	
	Average resting heart rate	
	Average distance	
	Total distance	
	Average time	
	Total time	
	Average zone	
	Average speed	
	Maximum speed	
	Average inclination	
	Average RPE	

Fitness Test

	Last Month	Target	Actual	Next Mth's Target
Working heart rate: after 4 minutes				
after 8 minutes				
after 12 minutes				
Recovery heart rate: at course completion				
1 minute after completion				
2 minutes after completion				
3 minutes after completion				
Time to cycle 3 miles/5km				
Completion time				

Total your weekly results and divide by the number of weeks to get your average.

Average monthly mood   1–5 [ ]

Average monthly appetite   1–5 [ ]

Average monthly energy level   1–5 [ ]

Average monthly stress level   1–5 [ ]

Average weekly hours of sleep [ ]

Average monthly sleep quality   1–5 [ ]

Average monthly soreness level   1–5 [ ]

Next Month's Targets

	Next Month's Target
Weight	
Resting heart rate	
Distance	
Time	
Zone	
Average speed	
Maximum speed	
Inclination	
RPE	

Injuries/Illnesses

Monthly Notes

Monthly Summary

MONTH **12** DATE [/ /]

Targets Versus Results

Last Month's Target		This Month's Result
	Average weight	
	Average resting heart rate	
	Average distance	
	Total distance	
	Average time	
	Total time	
	Average zone	
	Average speed	
	Maximum speed	
	Average inclination	
	Average RPE	

Fitness Test

	Last Month	Target	Actual	Next Mth's Target
Working heart rate: after 4 minutes				
after 8 minutes				
after 12 minutes				
Recovery heart rate: at course completion				
1 minute after completion				
2 minutes after completion				
3 minutes after completion				
Time to cycle 3 miles/5km				
Completion time				

Total your weekly results and divide by the number of weeks to get your average.

Average monthly mood 1–5 [ ]

Average monthly appetite 1–5 [ ]

Average monthly energy level 1–5 [ ]

Average monthly stress level 1–5 [ ]

Average weekly hours of sleep [ ]

Average monthly sleep quality 1–5 [ ]

Average monthly soreness level 1–5 [ ]

Next Month's Targets

	Next Month's Target
Weight	
Resting heart rate	
Distance	
Time	
Zone	
Average speed	
Maximum speed	
Inclination	
RPE	

Injuries/Illnesses

Monthly Notes

End-of-Year Assessment

DATE [/ /]   **AGE** [ ]

Record your results from your final ride in the logbook here and measure them against your initial ride.

Targets		Results		Difference [+/-]
Weight		Weight		
Resting heart rate		Resting heart rate		
Total distance		Total distance		
Total time		Total time		
Average zone		Average zone		
Average speed		Average speed		
Maximum speed		Maximum speed		
Inclination		Inclination		
RPE		RPE		

Yearly Averages			
Resting heart rate		Maximum speed	
Distance		Zone	
Time		Inclination	
Average speed		RPE	

Cardiovascular Fitness Test and Endurance	Current	Difference [+/-]
Resting heart rate		
Working heart rate: after 4 minutes		
after 8 minutes		
after 12 minutes		
Recovery heart rate: at course completion		
1 minute after completion		
2 minutes after completion		
3 minutes after completion		
Time to cycle 3 miles/5km		
Completion time		

Current Personal Summary

Strength level | 1–5 |

Endurance level | 1–5 |

Satisfaction with fitness | 1–5 |

Satisfaction with weight | 1–5 |

Quality of diet | 1–5 |

Energy level | 1–5 |

Sleep quality | 1–5 |

Stress level | 1–5 |

Mood level | 1–5 |

Personal Bests

End-of-Year Personal Summary

Yearly Heart-Rate Graph

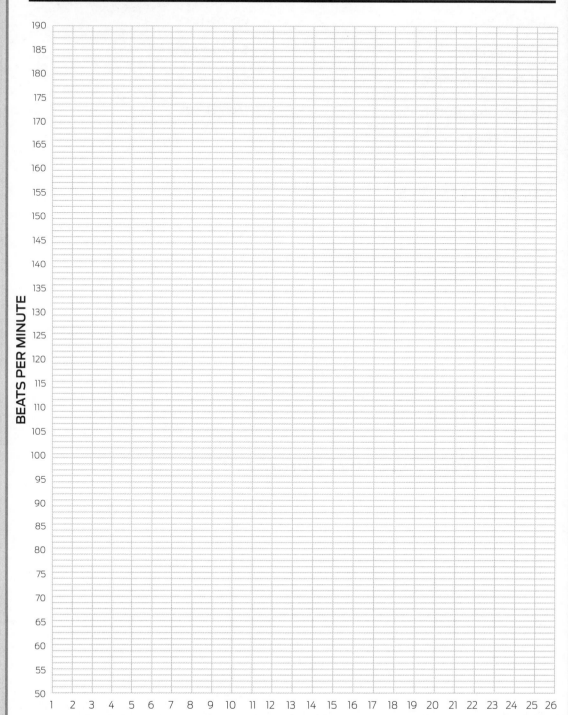

BEATS PER MINUTE

190
185
180
175
170
165
160
155
150
145
140
135
130
125
120
115
110
105
100
95
90
85
80
75
70
65
60
55
50

1 2 3 4 5 6 7 8 9 10 11 12 13 14 15 16 17 18 19 20 21 22 23 24 25 26

WEEK

Record your average weekly resting and maximum heart rates and graph your progress throughout the year.

BEATS PER MINUTE

WEEK

Training and Pre-Ride Checklist

No matter how well organized you are, there's always the possibility you could forget something. Use this checklist to ensure you don't forget anything important before your ride. You may not need everything on the list, but it pays to be prepared for anything!

Essentials

bike	
helmet	

Clothing

t-shirt/jersey	
tights	
shorts	
socks	
shoes	
gloves	
jacket	
wet-weather protective gear	

Safety

sunglasses	
sunscreen	
bike lock	
course map/area map	
cream/heat ointment	
petroleum jelly	
first aid kit	
medical information/emergency contact card	

Repair

patch kit	
tools	
spare cogs	
spare tube	
pump	
lubricant	

Extras

water bottle	
water/energy drink	
food/energy bars	
towel/wipes	
watch	
power meter/cycling computer	

Pre-ride Inspection

Always check that your bike is working properly and correctly adjusted before every ride. For your own safety, if something on this checklist doesn't pass inspection, repair it before you ride.

Check:

Tire pressure	
Tire condition	
Handlebar and seat height	
Lights and reflectors	
Chain tension	
Brakes and quick-release levers	
Lubrication	
Bolt tightness	